Frabato The Magician

22:3 Magic Mirror
25B Inconspicuous Behavior
32T D1
41 Walls covered with dark blue velvet
36:1 Man with a long chin.
59:5 Invisible Fluid.
68B 23rd of June?
69:2 your demons pin number?
WORD. DIVINE PROVIDENCE
108B Frabato & YOGIC ASANA.
WORD PROFESSOR.
112 The state of utter loneliness
115 Dangerous magical relationships.
122B Annihilation of Individuality?
127:1 From Belief to Knowledge *?
128:T The Gentleman's Agreement?
* 143-44
144:1 Laws of Gentleman's Agreement.
164:1 WORD psychoanalysis
32:2 ELLI / ELLA?
131:1 The Karma of the physical body
109:2 Spiritual Ability.
12:1 A special kind of Brass?
78B THE CANCELLER?
34:2 THE TOUCHING OF THE TIE SYNDROME

About the Author

Franz Bardon was born on December 1, 1909, in Katherein, near Opava in the present-day Czech Republic. He died on July 10, 1958, in Brno, also in the Czech Republic. He attended public school in Opava, and after that apprenticed as a mechanic. His stage name was "Frabato," which is an abbreviation of **Franz-Bardon-Troppau-Opava**.[1]

The special nature of this work required serious consideration before I published it under the name of Franz Bardon; the importance of the subject matter finally decided the issue. To pay tribute to truth, I should not like to conceal from the reader the fact that, in actuality, Franz Bardon supplied only the framework of facts for this book. Being pressed for time, he left its entire completion and embellishment to his secretary, Otti Votavova. Unfortunately, Bardon's posthumous manuscript was not ready for print, and therefore I had to revise it.

I would like to pass on some of the information which, according to Otti Votavova, she received directly from Franz Bardon. According to her, Adolf Hitler was a member of a 99 Lodge. Besides this, Hitler and some of his confidants were members of the Thule Order, which was simply the external instrument of a group of powerful Tibetan black magicians which used the members of the Thule Order for their own purposes. Hitler also employed a number of doubles on various occasions as camouflage.

---

[1] Troppau is the German name for the Czech city of Opava; because of the particulars of the region's history, many locations in the present-day Czech Republic have both Czech and German names.

Franz Bardon was brought to the Nazis' attention through the negligence of his student and friend, Wilhelm Quintscher (Rah Omir Quintscher). Quintscher had not destroyed his correspondence with Bardon, although he had been asked by Bardon to do so; that is how the National Socialists became aware of him.

While they were being flogged, Quintscher lost his self-control. He uttered a Kabbalistic formula, whereupon the torturers were immediately paralyzed completely. When he later neutralized the effect of the formula, he was shot in revenge.

Franz Bardon was offered high positions in the Third Reich by Adolf Hitler, but only in exchange for his help in winning the war with his magical abilities. Furthermore, Franz Bardon was expected to reveal to Hitler the location of the other ninety-eight lodges throughout the world. When he refused to help, he was exposed to the cruelest torture. Among other things, they performed operations on him without anesthetizing him. They forged iron rings around his ankles and fixed heavy iron balls to them.

Franz Bardon shared the fate of his fellow prisoners in Nazi concentration camps for three and a half years. In 1945, shortly before the war ended, he was sentenced to death. However, before the sentence could be carried out the prison in which he was being held was bombed. He was rescued from the heavily damaged building by some Russian fellow prisoners and succeeded in hiding from the police in his native country until the end of the war. He then worked his way back to his home town.

After the war, Franz Bardon used his magical abilities to determine that Adolf Hitler had escaped abroad, and that he had undergone a number of surgical operations on his face so as not to be recognized.

The photographs of Hermes Trismegistos, Lao-tse, Mahum Tah-Ta and Shambalah presented in this volume were originally published in the book *Das Buch vom Buddha das Westens,* by Hans Albert Müller (*Verlag des Ordens der*

Weltvollendung, 1930). This fact became known to me only recently; the photos were first painted by a mediumistic artist from the magic mirror of Franz Bardon.

This is the end of Otti Votavova's recital of facts. In the many years of my acquaintance with her I was able to convince myself of her love of truth.

In his book *The Practice of Magical Evocation*, Franz Bardon has written in some detail concerning the fact that certain disadvantages must always be taken into account when any kind of pact is made. Anyone who has thoroughly studied the occult sciences will not find it difficult to judge lodges, orders, sects and groups. One should always be on one's utmost guard wherever money or oaths are demanded in exchange for spiritual instruction, and wherever the secrets are kept by the higher degrees and concealed from the lower ones.

Evidence regarding the events related in this book will be reserved for people trained and developed in magic. Humankind will have to resign itself to the fact that a great deal of evidence concerning the workings of our cosmos can only be furnished through spiritual means.

Wuppertal, June 1979
Dieter Rüggeberg

Franz Bardon

Frabato The Magician

An Occult Novel

2002

Merkur Publishing, Inc.
Wisdom of the Occident

Title of the German original edition: *Frabato*
First German Edition 1979 by Dieter Rüggeberg Verlag
D–42035 Wuppertal, Germany
Published by arrangement with Dieter Rüggeberg Verlag,
Postfach 130844, D–42035 Wuppertal, Germany
First English Edition 1982 by Dieter Rüggeberg Verlag

First Softbound Printing 2002 by Merkur Publishing, Inc.
Translated by Gerhard Hanswille; Edited by Kenneth Johnson

ISBN 1-885928-15-7

Printed in the United States of America
Cover design by Reed Perkins

Merkur Publishing, Inc.
PO Box 171306
Salt Lake City, UT 84117
(800) 204-2473

email: merkurbook@aol.com
www.merkurpublishing.com

Contents

Chapter I

The overcrowded lecture room of the clubhouse was full of excitement, for the suspense aroused in the first part of the program had caused a heated discussion among the members of the audience.

"Who is this Frabato?"

"Here are the facts at last!"

"It is all just tricks and illusion!"

Could anyone trust his own senses? A mixture of delight and enthusiasm filled everyone's mind.

The sound of a bell signaled the end of the intermission. The rows quickly filled again; all conversation subsided and, as the lights dimmed in the lecture hall, the curtain slowly rose.

The setting of the stage gave no impression whatsoever that a magician was about to begin his performance, for the usual paraphernalia of a magic show was nowhere to be seen. A large crystal chandelier illuminated the stage, in the center of which stood a round table covered with a dark-blue brocade tablecloth. Ten chairs had been placed behind the table in a semi-circle, while to the right of the table the audience could see a single armchair.

Frabato entered with an easy stride; he greeted the audience with a casual bow. Although his tuxedo added a serious tone, his friendly smile placed at ease those who would typically be quite terrified by the notion of magical experiments. As the applause subsided, Frabato addressed the audience:

"Ladies and gentlemen — having explained to you the fundamentals of suggestion and autosuggestion during the first part of the program, and having demonstrated those principles, I would now like to move on to a different theme. Animal magnetism is of great importance to the very existence of humankind, and therefore I should not like to neglect the opportunity to introduce this power to you.

"Everything in this world is controlled by electric and magnetic forces. However, the ability of particular substances to accumulate and conduct such electrical and magnetic forces varies a great deal. This knowledge is of great importance when fashioning amulets — but we shall not go into detail about such matters at the moment. Instead, I will now explain the essence of magnetism and prove its existence with practical demonstrations.

"Animal magnetism is the most perfect element of life. It is the vital energy and the vital matter that forms the basis of all life on earth. This vital magnetism connects the earth with the zone which girdles the earth; this zone is often called the astral world or simply 'the beyond.' Vital magnetism also connects people to one another. A human being radiates an energy that is purely animal, and the power and purity of that energy are dependent upon the person's will, his characteristics and his mental maturity. His health depends upon these three qualities in turn.

"This magnetism is especially strong in people who consciously train their spirits and souls, who possess self-control and who understand how to master their fates. Through this vital energy they are able to strengthen their thoughts and the impulses of their will, and consequently to perform extraordinary deeds.

"Since animal magnetism is an objective force, it may be used for both positive and negative purposes. The saying 'As you sow, so shall you reap' is an expression of karmic law and justice; therefore, the true magician pursues only positive goals. A trained magician can be very successful in healing people with vital magnetism, and therefore I have always had a great personal interest in this phenomenon.

12

"Through a number of demonstrations, I intend to show you other secret qualities and forces connected with animal magnetism. For this purpose, I ask that three people from the audience join me on stage."

As Frabato waited, a murmur could be heard throughout the hall. Then, to encourage the audience, he said with a smile, "You need not be afraid. No one will be harmed. Just join me on the stage."

An attractive blonde stood up and, with hesitation, approached the stage. "Just look," Frabato said jokingly. "People always say that women are the weaker sex, but this lady has proved the contrary to all those gentlemen present in this hall." The audience laughed and instantly a young man hurried on stage, followed by an elderly woman.

"I am very grateful to you for your help," Frabato said to the volunteers. "Now, if you would be so kind, please place one of your personal belongings at my disposal for a short time on the table."

The blonde woman was the first; she put her silver wrist watch on the table. The young gentleman, a somewhat easy-going character, set his wallet beside the wrist watch. After an encouraging smile from Frabato, the elderly woman removed her necklace and added it to the two objects already on the table.

"By way of introduction," Frabato said, again addressing the audience, "I will now give you a brief demonstration of psychometry. This will prove to you that every human being leaves traces of his essence on those objects which have come into contact with his body. The age of the object is of no consequence. Even if an object were several thousand years old, everything imprinted upon it would be clearly revealed to my clairvoyant eyes. With the help of these three objects, I shall now prove to you the validity of this statement."

Frabato approached the table, took the silver wrist watch, and walked slowly to and fro a few times, deeply absorbed in thought. Suddenly he stopped, put the wrist watch to his forehead, and for a few moments remained completely still, a distant expression in his eyes. Then, as if awakening from a dream, he turned towards the blonde.

"You seem to seriously doubt my abilities, otherwise you would certainly not have come on stage with a watch that you borrowed from your sister. I am able to see that you wear it quite often without her knowledge since she works in Berlin. This watch was a confirmation gift from an aunt who died in an accident, and that is why your sister herself does not wear it anymore. It would certainly cause some ill feelings if she knew that you wear the watch."

One could plainly see the embarrassment and shame reflected on the woman's face, making it clear that Frabato was indeed correct.

Suddenly the young man tried to take his wallet from the table. Frabato was quicker than he and picked up the wallet, weighing it carefully.

"You do not seem to have a clear conscience, sir. Therefore, I will ascertain the cause."

After studying the wallet closely for some seconds, he continued:

"You are still young — but you go a bit too far in deceiving two girls. The one whose photograph you carry in your wallet only began to favor you with her affections after you built imaginary castles in the air for her — she considers them real. Besides this, I see a love letter to another girl whom you met recently at some event, and who aroused your attention with her flirtatious behavior. Your private affairs are not my concern, but I can assure you that you will not be happy with either of the two ladies."

The young man became quite embarrassed, realizing he had been exposed. With an obvious sense of insecurity, he said, "I should not like to live near you. I should not feel safe with my most intimate thoughts."

Frabato put the wallet back on the table. Next, he picked up the necklace and let it glide through his fingers as if he were examining it.

"I could write a whole novel about this piece of jewelry," he said to its owner, "for it carries the imprint of both good and bad times. Its first owners were wealthy French aristocrats who went to the guillotine during the revolution. This necklace has brought each of its owners a certain measure of misfortune — after your husband was killed in the Great War, you had to live on a small military pension for a very long time. I see the necklace at the pawnbroker's twice, but you always managed to get it back."

Frabato was silent now, for the woman began to weep. The audience sat motionless after this heavy account of fate. Frabato put the necklace back on the table and again addressed the audience:

"Ladies and gentlemen, as I have just proven to you, every object carries its own history with it. Moreover, you have had an opportunity to convince yourselves of the various applications of clairvoyance."

Enthusiastic applause from the audience relieved the heightened tension. When all was quiet again, Frabato continued, "I should now like to ask the three volunteers to leave the hall, accompanied by two neutral observers."

A gentleman wearing glasses and a woman in a dark dress agreed to accompany the volunteers.

"To demonstrate to you the effects of magnetism in connection with will power, I shall now charge these objects with very particular effects which will occur immediately once someone touches them. I should like to hear from you what sort of effects you would like them to be. Please tell me which responses these three objects on the table ought to evoke upon the first person who touches them."

A gentleman in the middle of the hall suggested that the silver watch should cause loud laughter. Frabato agreed. The second suggestion, too, was agreed upon by all: that the wallet should cause weeping and tears.

It remained to make a suggestion regarding the necklace. A woman in the first row spoke up:

"Since this necklace has brought misfortune to a number of people already, I suggest that it be prepared in a manner whereby the first person who touches it will be forced to throw it away in antipathy."

Prolonged applause made further discussion unnecessary.

Frabato arranged the three objects on the table, leaving a well defined space between each. He stood completely motionless before each item and, with intense concentration, made a few gestures with his right hand over them. Then he addressed the audience again.

"Ladies and gentlemen, my work is done. In order that no one may claim that I work with hypnosis, I shall now go to the refreshment room. Two independent observers from the audience will accompany me there, and then bring back the volunteers, asking them to take their possessions. I will return to the stage in exactly ten minutes."

Frabato left the hall accompanied by two gentlemen, who returned with the volunteers and their escorts shortly thereafter. Somewhat doubtful, the blonde woman, the young man and the elderly woman approached the table. The audience grew tense with anticipation.

Arriving on the stage, the volunteers were informed by the gentlemen accompanying them that they could now reclaim their possessions and return to their seats.

The blonde was in a hurry. With a quick motion she grasped her wrist watch and, in the next moment, broke into an infectious laugh which quickly spread throughout the entire audience.

As she walked back to her seat, the other two volunteers stood there hesitantly, somewhat astonished. Then the young man reached for his wallet. He had not finished putting it back into his pocket before tears began to roll down his cheeks and, shaken by a sob, he hid his face in his hands. He recovered after a few moments and left the stage accompanied by applause.

Because of the strange things her fellow volunteers had just experienced, the elderly lady stood before her necklace completely at a loss. At last she reached out bravely for it, but then flung it immediately into a corner of the stage. As, still astonished by her own reaction, she accepted the return of the necklace from a helpful gentleman, cheers rang out from the audience.

As there was no one left on stage, the door to the hall opened and Frabato reappeared, welcomed enthusiastically by the audience. With a spring in his step he made his way to the stage, and said with a smile, "What a great atmosphere here! You seem to have enjoyed the performance. Now I would like to ask ten people who are afflicted with some kind of illness to come onto the stage."

Quite a number of spectators hurried to the stage. The ten chairs behind the table were quickly taken, and there were many who were forced to return to their seats.

Frabato went from one to the next, pausing before each person for a few seconds, and then, using the appropriate medical terminology, described each individual's illness. The afflicted showed surprise at his quick and correct diagnoses. He then addressed them:

"My dear visitors, I can see from your expressions that you have a great deal of confidence in me and that you expect a complete recovery, or at least relief, from your illness. With the help of my trained will power, I shall try to help everyone as much as possible. Although a complete cure may not be possible immediately for severe cases, I can at least promise everyone a noticeable relief. Please remain seated calmly and in a relaxed and comfortable position."

He requested silence from the audience, too, and sat down

on a chair so that everyone could see him clearly. Frabato closed his eyes, and in a few seconds seemed to have gone completely rigid. After a minute had passed, he opened his eyes again, jumped up from his chair, and asked his patients how they felt.

"Excellent! Wonderful! What a relief!" were the responses. The patients' faces had brightened under the influence of increased vitality, and each of them expressed his personal thanks before leaving the stage.

"This is the end of today's show," Frabato announced. "However, I should not neglect to invite everyone to my next performance, which will take place the day after tomorrow. Good night to you all."

He went to his dressing room while the applause continued. Shortly afterwards, he left the auditorium through a side door and took a taxi to his hotel. Arriving there, he ordered a refreshment and then locked the door to his room.

He had just completed the meditations he performed every night before going to bed when someone knocked on his door. The bellboy apologized for such a late disturbance, and informed him that a gentleman who urgently wanted to speak with him was waiting in the hotel lobby.

Thoughtfully, Frabato read the peculiar business card the bellboy had brought him. In the center of the card was a large circle; within this was a smaller circle, above which was a triangle with two intersecting lines. On either side of the large circle there were two dragons; on the back of the card there was only the name "Hermes." The card was printed in gold.

After a short consideration, Frabato instructed the young man to escort the late visitor up to his room. A few moments later he welcomed a well-dressed gentleman with graying hair.

It was almost morning when the visitor left the hotel. His distraught face seemed to suggest that he had experienced something quite extraordinary.

18

Chapter II

The members of the secret F.O.G.C. Lodge, greatly feared in occult circles, had gathered for a general meeting in Dresden. The meeting hall was in a large villa, hidden in the midst of a private park behind a tall hedge and large trees. The Grand Master of the lodge had invited ninety-eight of the ninety-nine members to attend. Long before the meeting commenced, the members had taken their places at two long tables.

All conversation in the hall became muted when the Grand Master entered accompanied by his second-in-command, who also acted as Secretary. There was a platform opposite the hall's entrance where the Grand Master sat down behind a desk. He rang a bell and at once there was complete silence. He addressed the brethren of the lodge in an intense, penetrating voice:

"My dear brothers, I hereby open today's meeting, and I am pleased that you have all accepted my invitation. As you know, according to the laws of the lodge a general meeting such as this is only declared in very special cases. You may have already noticed that Brother Silesius is not present. Unfortunately, he has been found guilty of betraying lodge secrets and, as Point Number One of the agenda, we will discuss his sentence. Point Number Two concerns Frabato the Magician, who is becoming so well-known here in Dresden.

"My dear brothers, you all know that Brother Silesius has reached the twenty-fifth degree of initiation in our lodge, and therefore must have been fully aware of his offences. His excessive zeal seduced him to reveal to one of his friends the rituals we use to invoke the elemental beings. According to the laws of our lodge, the breaking of an oath and the disclosure of secrets are punishable by death. However, the sentence will only become final after a secret vote by all members present. Although the person in question is my friend, I cannot excuse his behavior, and therefore I leave him to your judgment."

A nervous tension swiftly overwhelmed the brotherhood; the members whispered excitedly among themselves. Some displayed anger, others sat as if paralyzed. The Secretary handed out envelopes with a blank piece of paper to everyone present. A simple "yes" or "no" would determine the life or death of their lodge brother. "Yes" would mean death by psychic assault, "no" would mean freedom and life.

Many wrote down their judgments quickly, others hesitated for a moment, and a few were unable even to control their trembling hands as they wrote down their verdicts. Despite the fact that Silesius had been well-liked by many of them, a false sense of compassion would be misplaced, for the betrayal of lodge secrets could be very dangerous for all concerned.

At last the Secretary collected all the envelopes in a small wooden box, took out the slips of paper, and divided them into two small piles according to the answers given. The brethren watched silently.

The Secretary counted the slips of paper very carefully and made a note of the result. His normally rosy face grew pale as he verified the result once again. He then submitted his note to the Grand Master, who stared at the numbers, his face reflecting shock — a good friend had just been sentenced to death. He rose, quite disturbed.

"My dear brothers," he said in a trembling voice, "unfortunately the voting has gone against Silesius, who has been irrevocably sentenced to death by a margin of fifty-one to forty-seven. According to our laws, this sentence must be executed within a month, but since, by using his occult faculties, Brother Silesius will learn what is in store for him

20

and will probably try to evade death, we shall execute the sentence within twenty-four hours. The friend to whom he betrayed the secrets of the lodge will suffer the same fate. I ask the twenty-one brethren who are masters in telepathic combat to remain here after the meeting and assist me in the psychic attack."

Although the verdict had deeply shaken the Grand Master, he quickly regained his composure and continued in a calmer voice.

"Since Point Number One of the agenda has been settled, let us now deal with the case of Frabato. Some of the brethren present attended his performances and were able to convince themselves of his abilities at close range. It has been proven that he works without the aid of conventional tricks. His experiments succeeded beyond all expectation; yes, they were even better than what many of our own brethren would be able to accomplish. Hermes, one of our more versatile brothers, paid a visit to Frabato in order to test him. He will now tell you of his experience."

The distinguished gentleman who had visited Frabato late at night now rose from amongst the brethren.

"I chose the best astrological hour for my visit to Frabato. I also took into account the correspondences of the elements in order to place myself in a strong initial position. Besides this, I hoped he would be exhausted after the performance he had just given; that would have been to my advantage. I explained the unusual time of my visit by telling him I had a journey to make which could not be postponed. Upon hearing this, Frabato looked at me sharply and then smiled faintly without uttering a word.

"I then painted a very colorful picture of our lodge membership, pointed out its many advantages, and promised him a large sum of money from our funds should he decide to join. But Frabato completely ignored my proposals and started to talk about his journeys, his performances and successes in many cities and towns. He was able to arouse my curiosity so strongly that I almost forgot the reason for my visit.

"In time I interrupted him and tried to direct his attention to my offer. He rose and pulled a suitcase out from under his bed saying, 'Now let us have a look at what the Akashic records have to say about your lodge.'

"As you know, my dear brothers, I am well acquainted with occult methods and practices; therefore I was determined to use all my powers to prevent Frabato's experiment. But as soon as the notion entered my mind, he said to me, as if by chance, 'Dear Mr. Hermes, my experiments depend purely upon my will power and cannot be influenced or prevented by you. They will succeed whether you actively oppose them or not.'

"I felt that Frabato could see right through me, and surmised that I would have no chance against him, so I watched his preparations intently. First he cleaned his hands carefully, took a small bottle out of his suitcase, and applied a few drops to his hands. No doubt it was prepared from the essences of certain plants, for a pleasant fragrance permeated the room. He then took a small lamp out of a little box and put it on the table. Then, from a second box, he brought forth a glass ball about twenty centimeters in diameter and placed it on a stand on the table. When I asked him what purpose this glass ball served, Frabato laughed and replied, 'If there were any clairvoyants in your lodge, and if they really possessed the knowledge which you attempt or pretend to have, then they would know that this is a magic mirror. This sphere contains a liquid, the particular composition of which requires not only patient work but excellent magical abilities as well.'

"I realized my knowledge was no match for Frabato's, and therefore thought it better to wait in silence. We were about a meter away from the sphere. Frabato then lit the lamp and switched off the electric lights, asking that I remain quiet under all circumstances. All the colors of the spectrum emanated from the reflecting light of the sphere. The little flame illuminated the sphere and the space around it, and also emitted a certain fragrance. I thought at once that the fuel of the lamp must be impregnated with a special essence, but I said nothing. However, Frabato read my mind and said, 'I can perceive your thoughts as clearly as if you were speaking them aloud, so just tell me if you have a question. Is the quick reading of thoughts not one of the exercises in your lodge?'

"I was enraged; but I tried to control myself, for I felt that nothing remained hidden from this man.

"'I am going to show you a film, and then you can judge for yourself whether it is really advantageous to be a member of your lodge,' he continued.

"I watched each of his movements attentively, to be sure that he was not employing any tricks. He rolled up the sleeves of his shirt and sat down beside me in front of the sphere. Then he stretched both his hands towards the glass ball, his fingers slightly splayed. A grayish-white light escaped from the tips of his fingers and was absorbed by the sphere which, a few moments later, began to illuminate everything with a fluorescent ball of light the color of a fiery opal. Frabato then brought the transmission of light to an end and remarked that it would even be possible to photograph the images in this magic ball. I was by that time in some suspense as he said:

"'Next we shall look behind the scenes of your esteemed Grand Master's life. This will offer you the opportunity to become acquainted with both the positive and negative aspects of his character. I hope you will be able to withstand what you see, and that you will not fall asleep.'

"Although my nerves were taut with curiosity, the wonderful light of the sphere seemed, in fact, to have already had a tiring effect on me. I had no wish to appear foolish and, by gathering all my will power, I succeeded in staying awake for the entire demonstration.

"The opalescent light illuminated the entire room; however, it gradually began to vaporize inside the sphere. There were multi-colored clouds floating within, but they soon dissolved and were replaced by a violet hue. Then the image of our Grand Master condensed, as in a panorama. The pictures moved swiftly from his early childhood to the present day. Many of the events I saw shocked me; a shiver ran down my spine. The most incredible pictures were unveiled there, and I could not evade them for I was unable to move."

The color of the Grand Master's face changed a few times. When Hermes began to describe some of the more startling events of the Grand Master's life as revealed to him in the magic mirror, the Grand Master discreetly gave him to understand that this was not desirable. Hermes understood, and skillfully moved on to more general topics.

"After I had been given the opportunity to follow in this magical manner the destiny of our Grand Master and that of our lodge up until the present, Frabato made a circle over the sphere with his right hand and, with his right forefinger, drew a figure which I did not recognize. The images disappeared.

"Somewhat relieved, I wanted to turn away from the sphere, when suddenly the shape of our Secretary condensed inside of it. His life, too, rolled off like a film in front of my eyes. Every crime of the lodge was revealed without mercy. In this manner, Frabato continued to disclose to me the lives of the seven eldest members of our lodge. When he wanted to show me my own life, I felt so ill at ease and ashamed that he refrained. After he had drawn another figure over the sphere and murmured a formula, the light finally faded.

"Frabato rose, switched on the electric light and extinguished the lamp. Silently, he replaced the sphere and the lamp in their boxes and locked everything away in the suitcase. When he had finished, he asked me with a scornful air, 'Now, sir, do you still wish to recommend something like that to me?'

"I was completely confused by the magical power of the man, and hence incapable of uttering a word. I grabbed my hat and coat and hurried to the door without daring to make any comment. I did not even put my things on until I reached the corridor, and then I left the hotel in haste. My belief in the power of our lodge was strongly shaken, and I could find no rest that night."

The account of this experience with Frabato made a great impression on everyone present. No one dared to move; a dead quiet weighed upon them heavily. The Grand Master rose hurriedly and broke the depressive silence with a sharp voice.

"Dear brother Hermes, in the name of our brotherhood I thank you for your efforts during this difficult mission. I consider Frabato's revelations of the activities of our lodge, and of some of its highest and eldest members, a great insult. I swear by the name of the Lord of Darkness that we shall release all the furies of hell on Frabato, so that he will learn what he is dealing with! I shall not allow our lodge to be insulted! He shall be subjected to the fatal power of our vibrations until he perishes most miserably! May he be damned in the name of Satan, in the name of Ashtaroth, and in the name of Belial!"

The enraged Grand Master shouted his terrible curse; it was the most severe malediction he had ever been driven to utter in public. No victim could escape such a curse, or evade the persecutions of the Order.

After requesting that the twenty-one executioners of the lodge remain, he thanked the assembly for their co-operation and closed the session by ringing the bell. Some took their leave after giving the lodge's secret sign, then disappeared into the city traffic. Inconspicuous behavior was one of the

25

strictest rules of the lodge, and necessary in order not to arouse the attention of the general public or the curious.

The Grand Master took his seat again, a smile of contentment on his face. He felt instinctively that this Frabato was a powerful opponent, but there was no turning back after uttering his curse. This battle would have to be fought to the end, even if it endangered his own life. Under no circumstances could he allow his authority over the brethren to be lost or even undermined.

The remaining brethren discussed at length how Frabato could best be attacked. Many different suggestions were made and recorded in shorthand by the Secretary in order to be put to a vote at the next meeting.

The case of Brother Silesius was to be settled in the traditional manner, and thus it was not necessary to discuss the matter further. Upon a signal from the Grand Master, the Secretary left the hall and went into a room situated at the back of the house. This room, which had no windows and the doors of which were equipped with special safety locks, contained oddly-shaped cupboards in which various magical equipment was stored.

The black magician opened an iron trunk and removed a medium-sized coffin. Contained therein was the wax figure of a man. Then, from a safe in the wall, he took a large brown bottle sealed with a glass stopper. He placed the objects on a table in the middle of the room. With a pocket knife, he loosened a little plate from the skull-pan of the wax figure, revealing a small opening. A canal the width of a finger ran down the length of the figure's back.

The Secretary then unsealed and opened the brown bottle and carefully poured as much liquid into the opening of the figure as was necessary to fill it to the head. Then he covered the opening again with the plate and fastened it with liquid wax. He shaped and smoothed the wax, thus concealing any trace of the opening. He closed the bottle and sealed it with the help of his signet ring.

There was a smooth circle on the figure's chest, in which the Secretary now wrote the victim's lodge name. He took a diary from the cupboard and, in the lodge's secret code, entered the day's date and the name of the man to be executed, then put it back in its place. Following this, he opened the drawer of a desk in which were daggers of various lengths, shapes, and strengths. From this collection he selected a dagger which was small and sharp. After ascertaining that he had not forgotten anything, he placed both the wax figure and the dagger in the coffin, then left the room.

With the coffin under his arm, the Secretary carefully locked the door and went back to the assembly hall. The Grand Master took the coffin. He made certain the figure had been correctly prepared, then placed the coffin upright on the floor. Three large candles were lit, and the electric lights were turned off.

The twenty-one executioners now formed a circle around the figure, the Grand Master remaining outside the ring to function as an observer. The brethren joined hands and walked slowly around the figure seven times, staring at it intently without interruption. They began to breathe rhythmically in unison, raising and lowering their arms. Each time they exhaled and lowered their arms, they repeated a formula, louder and louder each time.

The entire ceremony was repeated and the pace quickened. Patches of fog were beginning to form around the figure, condensing into clouds, and eventually solidifying to a spherical shape which completely engulfed the wax figure. The grayish color which had been visible at the beginning now turned to red. Dark figures seemed to be condensing therein, and, after a few moments, the cloud formation took on a fiery red color. The Grand Master approached it, making a sign in the air with his right hand. Then he broke the chain formed by the brethren. Slowly, the red cloud disappeared into the wax figure. The exhausted brethren sat down at the table.

The Grand Master seized the figure and placed it in the open coffin. Solemnly, he lit the candles in the candlestick holders which stood at either end of the casket. There was complete silence in the hall. The twenty-one brothers were rigid with suspense; they dared not move.

The Grand Master's face froze into a mask. His eyes were cold and fixed as he reached for the waiting dagger. His hand rose slowly, his eyes riveted upon their object — the circle with the victim's name. Then the blade flashed in the candle-light and pierced the figure's chest. A crash of thunder shook the hall to its foundations; an enormous roar filled the air, as though a storm were about to erupt. This lasted for a few moments, then faded gradually to a distant rumble and finally subsided altogether, giving way to an uncanny stillness.

The Grand Master's face mirrored triumph, for he felt that he was master over life and death. Relieved, he let himself fall back into a nearby chair.

Although all those present were familiar with such phenomena, they were nevertheless stricken with terror every time they performed rituals of this kind. The Secretary was the first to recover. He switched on the light, extinguished the candles, and removed the coffin.

The other brethren also regained their composure. The phenomenon they had experienced was proof that the purpose of their efforts had been achieved. They talked quietly among themselves as their Master entered the particulars of the magical operation in the diary. He then rose and addressed them.

"My dear brothers, I thank you all for your successful participation. Our Brother Silesius died of a heart attack at precisely 10:00 P.M. We have executed the sentence in accordance with the regulations of our holy order, and have thus taken revenge for the treason he committed. His friend has been sentenced to death as well, but his execution will take place at a later date. We shall discuss the reasons for this at our next meeting. The admission of a new member to replace Brother Silesius can be combined with the St. John's Day meeting. I expect to see you here tomorrow evening at eight o'clock. The case of Frabato is on the agenda. Today's session is now closed. Good night."

One after the other, the brethren left the lodge and disappeared inconspicuously into the night.

*

The minute hand on the large electric clock in the railroad station was slowly moving towards 10:00. In the station concourse a number of travelers were waiting for the express train from Bad Schandau to Berlin. A voice on the loud-speaker announced the train's arrival, and those who were waiting went up to the platform quickly, for the train would stop in Dresden for only a few minutes.

Frabato was standing in front of the list of train sched-ules, making a few notes. Just as the express train arrived, he put his notebook back in his pocket. A compartment door opened directly in front of him and a young man in a travel-ing suit jumped out and hurried to the refreshment stand. He paid for a packet of biscuits and was on his way back to the train when, after a few steps, he suddenly reached for his chest with both hands and collapsed with a groan. He writhed in pain for just a few seconds, his face contorted in a spasm; then his body lay motionless.

Curious onlookers immediately gathered around him. The police arrived quickly and took the lifeless body to the station office. Someone called a doctor on the telephone and the eye-witnesses gave their statements.

Standing nearby, Frabato silently watched the course of

events. He knew instinctively that the unknown man had not died a natural death, and, as a magician, he knew as well that it was too late for help. Slowly, he left the station and walked towards the Leipzigerstrasse. After a stroll of about an hour he stopped in a little grove on the outskirts of the city and sat down to rest.

The night was wonderfully mild and the moon and stars were shining from a clear sky. Absorbed in meditation, he stayed there a while before starting to walk back to his hotel. He stopped a taxi near the Elbe harbor and got a ride the rest of the way.

It was two o'clock in the morning when he entered his room. He locked the door, pulled out his suitcase and set up his magic sphere. What he saw there confirmed his suspicion that the young man's death had been caused by a violent action on the part of the F.O.G.C. Lodge. Frabato locked the ball away in the suitcase and retired for the night.

Next morning he bought a copy of Dresden's largest daily newspaper and found what he was looking for on the front page. The following account was given under the headline "Death At Dresden Central Station":

"The popular author Dr. Alfred M. died suddenly at Central Station at ten o'clock last night. Our city mourns the sudden end of this young and promising talent whose works have been greeted with so much enthusiasm. His latest drama, *The Testament,* has only recently been printed. We shall keep this ambitious and talented man in our hearts in loyal remembrance."

Chapter III

As agreed upon, the twenty-one specialists in the art of psychic attack met with the Grand Master of the F.O.G.C. Lodge once again. First they dealt with the issue of Director Z., the president of a large bank who had received some important secrets of the twenty-eight degrees of the Lodge from Silesius. Since the director was not a member, he either had to become one or else forfeit his life. But his personality did not seem to fit in with the lodge, and consequently he was sentenced to death. As president of a large financial institution, Z. commanded a great deal of authority — hence it was decided that he should first be used as an instrument to procure large sums of money.

The lodge consisted primarily of powerful capitalists who had amassed their considerable possessions and wealth through occult means — which also allowed them to access major sources of capital even during hard times. They were prepared to employ any means to achieve their goals. A man's life meant little to them, and they were proficient at exploiting the legal machinery of the land for their own purposes. Their complex methods, training, and experience enabled them to carry on their criminal trade right under the public's nose without arousing any suspicion. Their work was facilitated by the fact that the German public paid no attention to research in the field of mental laws and powers.

The lodge gave public performances on the subject of occultism which were intended to convince the public that it was all just tricks and deception — for they knew full well that a general knowledge of occult philosophy would create a new social order that could greatly hinder their own goals. Besides this, their performances also functioned as a hedge against the possibility that they might be recognized by genuine, high-minded occultists who, if believed, might expose them to the world.

The work accomplished by Frabato, who was able so convincingly to demonstrate the existence of spiritual laws and powers, naturally aroused their hostility. If he had simply been one of the many pseudo-occultists who were then so popular, the lodge would have had no reason to intervene. The Grand Master in particular was full of hatred for Frabato, whom he could not forgive for revealing his own past to Brother Hermes. Therefore, the lodge members decided to use every means possible to prevent Frabato from continuing his lectures.

First, however, they made the necessary preparations for the death of Director Z. The Secretary went to the basement apartment to fetch Elli, the caretaker's daughter, who acted as their clairvoyant medium in various experiments. The girl lived there with her father, her mother having died several years before. Elli was eighteen and slender, with wavy brown hair and dark blue eyes. Although she did not like being a medium, she dared not refuse, for that would have cost her father his job.

After a few minutes, Elli appeared in the conference room accompanied by the Secretary. A signal was given and a sofa was placed in the center of the room, draped with a white silk cover. A second silk cover was kept ready nearby in case it became necessary to insulate the medium during the experiment.

The Grand Master gave the signal to begin the operation. Elli lay down on the sofa and the Secretary sat beside her on a chair. He looked into her eyes with a penetrating stare and whispered a few powerful suggestions. Within a few minutes Elli was in the first stages of hypnosis; with a number of magnetic strokes the magician succeeded in placing her into the deepest possible state. A few more strokes over her throat enabled her to speak during hypnosis.

Elli was so well trained in hypnotic states that she was able to carry out any command without difficulty. First she was ordered to find out, through a mental visit, what Frabato was doing at that very moment; she immediately reported that he was performing magical experiments on a stage. The Secretary hurriedly called her spirit back, afraid that Frabato would notice her and thus become aware of their present activities.

Elli was then ordered to report on the activities of Director Z. She responded at once that he was home reading the newspaper. Asked about other members of the director's family, the medium answered that there was no one else in the house.

Armed with this knowledge, the Grand Master made a sign and the brethren formed a circle around Elli and the Secretary. They charged the medium with magnetic fluid and, when the magnetic tension became strong enough, ordered her to make the director sleep and then to watch him constantly.

Through the medium's influence, Z. was seized by an overwhelming need for slumber. He had scarcely placed his head on the pillow before he fell fast asleep. Elli then did as she had been asked and informed the lodge members of the director's condition; she was then ordered to maintain contact with him. Through this magical assault, Z. had become a powerless instrument of the lodge.

The Secretary now engraved Z.'s name into a small wax disc prepared for that purpose. He placed it on the medium's solar plexus, thus forming a close spiritual connection with the victim. Next, the disc was placed on the girl's forehead for a few minutes in order to make the director's spirit susceptible to receiving orders by long-distance hypnosis. The Secretary touched the medium's ears and heart with the disc and then set it aside.

The circle formed by the brethren opened for a moment, the sofa with the medium on it was pushed aside, and the Grand Master now seated himself in the center of the ring. Next, the small wax disc was heated slightly, and then molded into the shape of a shell. Chanting a magic formula over and over again, the Grand Master placed himself in a state of trance so as to establish better psychic contact with the receiver, while he himself received the power to transmit energy from the circle formed by his brethren. In a voice filled with the power of suggestion he spoke into the small wax shell:

"A young man will come to your office tomorrow morning, promptly at 11:45. He will be wearing a dark suit and a red tie. This man will request a loan of a million marks for a building project in Switzerland. Being unable to resist, you will comply with his request. After he has stroked his forehead with his right hand three times, you will draw him a check for one million marks. Immediately after giving him the check, you will become irresistibly weary and fall asleep for exactly five minutes. When you awaken again, you will have forgotten everything that happened during the preceding hour. On no account will you be able to remember what the young man looked like. Every detail of the incident will have disappeared from your memory. From that moment on, you will begin to feel ill; you will even look sick, and you will be haunted with bad nerves. Your thoughts will be completely disordered for hours at a time, and you will become increasingly tired and depressed with each new day. You will get annoyed at every little thing and, consequently, you will find no rest. Nothing in this world will bring you joy. Finally, everyone who comes near you will find you unbearable, and after exactly fourteen days you will shoot yourself with your revolver."

Director Z. was regarded as a man of honor, well-known for his expertise in his field. Once, in London, he had been robbed; since then he had become very cautious and always kept a pistol ready at his bedside.

After the Grand Master concluded his hypnotic suggestions, he stared at the wax shell for a few more minutes, made a ritual sign, and wrapped the shell in a violet-colored silk cloth which the Secretary had given him.

The brethren's magic circle dissolved and they took their seats in the middle of the room. The sofa with the medium still in trance upon it was rolled back to the center of the room. The Secretary called her spirit back from the director's house and sent it to Frabato.

Frabato had by this time finished his performance and was visiting a good friend. The medium gave the brethren the exact address, and reported that the friend's family had already gone to bed and that the two men were talking about occult problems. Their talk was so lively that Frabato did not notice Elli watching him.

Having received this information, the Secretary called back the medium's spirit and, with a few magnetic strokes and the corresponding formula, brought Elli back to consciousness. She had no idea what she had achieved for the lodge — it was the extra income that appealed to her, although she found the peculiar circumstances of these meetings, on the whole, uncanny. The Secretary gently led her out of the room and gave her a few banknotes as a reward.

One of the secrets of the F.O.G.C. lodge members lay in their ability to put anyone to sleep, wake him up again, make him sick or healthy, and invigorate or kill him whenever they liked. The leading members of the lodge, however, had only acquired this knowledge by entering into a pact with a prince of demons. With their magical methods, they were able to influence any untrained person, who had no way of discovering the source of the influences at work upon him.

Frabato was a special case for the lodge, because he was acquainted with occult practices of every kind and, in addition to this, he was under the protection of the Brothers of Light. The F.O.G.C. Lodge knew about the Brothers of Light, but had no clear idea concerning the genuine extent of their powers. They decided to dispose of Frabato with a magical onslaught. After a short discussion, the Secretary went to the equipment room for the piece of apparatus they called the tepaphone. This device was placed in the center of the room. It was the lodge's most strictly guarded secret: a magical vibratory instrument which could emit fatal vibrations across any distance and constituted the deadliest weapon in the arsenal of the lodge.

If the picture or *mumia*[2] of any human being or animal were placed at the focal point of the tepaphone's vibrations, both the astral and physical bodies of that entity would be affected. Substances of any kind could be destroyed by this instrument from any distance. Furthermore, it served as a wireless transmitter of energy — something modern science could only dream about. Any kind of thought could be transmitted by the tepaphone as well. Finally, the device made it possible to cause nervous diseases and poisonings which puzzled the medical establishment. Typically, a picture or personal object was sufficient to establish contact with the intended victim — and remember, distance was of no consequence.

Since Frabato was a well-known personality, his picture was published in the newspapers from time to time, and it was easy for the F.O.G.C. Lodge to obtain a photograph for their purpose. The Grand Master now secured Frabato's photo to the focal point of the tepaphone's ray and ignited the fuel, a specially prepared mixture of high-percentage alcohol. At the same time, the other brethren formed a magic circle

---

[2] Any part of a person's body, such as nails, hair, bodily fluids, etc.

around the apparatus to begin combat telepathy by condensing the element of fire to the physical plane.

Black magicians usually resorted to this method of annihilation in cases where the victim possessed great occult abilities. The tepaphone was also frequently used for executions within the lodge. Thus far, the apparatus had never failed. Victims of the tepaphone were always diagnosed as having died from a stroke.

Frabato was still with his friend and their lively conversation continued. Both were so absorbed in their discussion that at first they did not notice the attack waged by the F.O.G.C. Lodge. Only when Frabato broke into a sudden excess of perspiration did he notice the extraordinary conditions around him. He walked up and down the room restlessly, seeking the cause of this unusual heat. He had never experienced anything like it before. The temperature in the room began to rise, affecting his friend as well.

Frabato quickly ascertained that the cause of the heat was not in his own physical body. His wrist watch and his ring burnt like fire on his skin. There was no doubt that some alien power was attempting to destroy him. He wanted to confront and fight this power, but the heat had already penetrated his body so severely that he was no longer able to concentrate. He sank helplessly into a chair.

His friend too was powerless against the projected force. What could one do in a case like this? To seek medical help would be senseless; what could doctors do against magical attacks?

The blood was almost boiling in Frabato's veins and, although he tried to resist, he could not effectively influence his body with his spirit. Desperate, Frabato called upon God for help and inspiration. He was convinced that, if he were not destined to end his incarnation this very hour, he would gain the help he needed.

Frabato's friend tried to magnetize him but had to retreat

because the extreme heat in the room had become almost unbearable. Suddenly, Frabato heard a voice within him calling, "Divert with water!"

He opened his lips and whispered, "Water! Plenty of water!"

His friend hurried out of the room, got a bucket and filled it with water. He quickly brought it back to Frabato, who listlessly dropped his left hand into it. Instantly he was relieved, and after a few minutes the clarity and power of his thoughts were restored.

The water was getting warmer and warmer; the friend had to get another bucket. The heat was thus conducted into the water for a long time, for the attack by the lodge continued unabated. But as the destructive vibrations were now passing through his body without any effect, Frabato soon felt strong enough to employ his clairvoyance. Spiritually, he pursued the destructive rays and discovered that they had their origin in the F.O.G.C. Lodge.

"You will regret having attacked me in this way," he thought. "As far as spiritual law permits, I shall work to defeat all your future plans."

As the tepaphone continued to emit its vibrations, Frabato continued to divert them into the water. Clairvoyantly, he observed without interruption the lodge's meeting until, after another hour, they broke their magic circle, removed his photo from the focal point, and extinguished the flame. He then watched as the Secretary locked the dangerous weapon back in the equipment room.

Afterwards, the lodge brethren talked among themselves for a short while, expressing their satisfaction that Frabato would no longer be able to do them any harm. They were already looking forward to the reports in the following day's newspapers informing the public of the well-known magician's sudden death and the cancellation of his performances. Another meeting was arranged for the next evening to celebrate the victory over their hated enemy. Then the sinister brotherhood disbanded for the day.

At that moment Frabato ended his observations. Since he had no acquaintances at his hotel, he accepted his friend's invitation to stay the night. Before retiring for the evening, though, he asked for a long piece of copper or iron wire and a sharp kitchen knife. His friend complied with Frabato's strange request; Frabato pulled the wire round his bed, connected both ends to the knife, and thrust it into the floor. Concentrating intently for a short while, he charged the wire with the power of protection in all three worlds. By so doing, he insulated himself securely against any injurious spiritual influences.

Then he went to bed. Frabato thanked God for his wonderful rescue and was soon sound asleep.

Chapter IV

The Grand Master of the F.O.G.C. Lodge sat in an elegant café on Pragerstrasse drinking a cup of coffee and perusing the pages of the Dresden papers.

"No notice of Frabato's death? It cannot be true! The tepaphone has never failed. Why else did we make a pact with the Prince of Demons?"

These were the thoughts that pounded through his mind.

Rage and disappointment strained his nerves. The brethren of the lodge wanted to celebrate their success that evening — and now this disgrace! Such a failure would no doubt shake some members' confidence in the power of the lodge. And above all, the Grand Master also realized that his own authority was greatly endangered.

He called to cancel the meeting for that evening and went to the lodge alone. As soon as he arrived, he went to a temple room used only for special magical operations carried out by the Grand Master himself.

The room had a single window that could be blacked out with a curtain. Near the east wall, a tetragonal column ornamented with magical signs served as an altar; the magical equipment had already been placed there. Above was a picture of Baphomet, the supreme god of black magicians. The walls were covered with dark-blue velvet. A large chandelier hung from the center of the light-blue ceiling. On the altar was a small magic lamp of the type called *lanterna magica* by occultists, shining with the seven colors of the rainbow and symbolizing an alliance with the spheres of the seven planets. In each corner of the room there were two very large candles in magnificent silver candlesticks. Although the room could be lit by electricity, only candles or spirit lamps were used for magical operations.

The Grand Master removed a dark-blue silk coat and a head scarf of the same color from a wardrobe. He closed the door to the temple, undressed, and put on the silk coat and scarf. The part of the scarf which covered his forehead was ornamented with an inverted pentagram embroidered in silver. A pair of violet silk slippers adorned his feet.

He opened a wall safe and took out an enormous white cover which he placed on the floor. The cover was embroidered with a multi-colored magical circle shaped like a snake whose back was ornamented with various names. There was a triangle just above the embroidered magic circle; it pointed upwards and there were letters at its corners. The center of the circle contained an inverted pentagram, embroidered in reddish-purple. Each corner of the pentagram was ornamented with a letter; taken altogether, they spelled out the word "Satan."

The Grand Master placed a dish of incense above the triangle and five flat candles round the circle. Then he carefully examined each piece of magical equipment again, for nothing must be forgotten during the invocations he intended to perform. Despite the protection he had acquired through his demonic pact, the least inattention could have severe consequences.

After adding incense powder, he lit the charcoal in the censer and a strong odor filled the room. Then he lit the candles and switched off the electric lights. The curtains kept out the daylight.

The Grand Master stepped majestically into the magic circle. His left hand gripped his magic sword, his right hand his magic wand. From his neck hung a *lamen*[3] engraved with the seal of the being he was about to invoke. Facing east, he recited the invocation formula with fervor:

"I am linked to you, salamanders and fire spirits of Hell. Your element is subject to me in all three worlds. I call upon you and invoke you, prince of the hellish fire spirits! I invoke you in the name of Satan, your holy master, who is your lord and ruler! As an ally of your master, I order you in his name to succumb to my will and to support my purposes through your element. I bind you to my magic sword and force you to absolute obedience. I demand from you that your fierce fire spirits be subjected to my will and that they assist me with my plans at whatsoever time. In the name of your highest lord and ruler, with whom I am joined by pact, I command you to persecute and destroy Frabato. Prince of the fire spirits of Hell! Appear here now, visibly before my circle, to confirm the reception of my orders!"

After the Grand Master had passionately recited this invocation, the flames of the candles rose high and the floor began to vibrate. A brightly shining ray appeared in the magic triangle and a shrill voice was heard:

"I have heard your request, great magician! We must serve you, for our most supreme lord is obligated to you. Therefore my subjects and I shall persecute Frabato wherever the influence of our element makes it possible. However, I cannot guarantee full success — because Frabato must fulfill a special mission on earth. His fate is not that of ordinary mortals!"

The shape of the being had become increasingly visible, and tongues of fire were dancing round it. An unbearable heat emanated from the apparition, whose power was so piercing

---

[3] For a detailed description of *lamens*, see Bardon's *Practice of Magical Evocation*, p. 66-9.

that the Grand Master himself felt he was in danger. He lifted his sword and directed its tip towards the entity. The fire-being vanished with the crackling of a thunderbolt, causing the ground beneath his feet to vibrate.

After resting and concentrating quietly for a few moments, the black magician faced south:

"You, forces of the element of air! My whole being is now in contact with your element. King of the demonic beings of the air, heed my call and obey my will. As an ally of your highest lord, I invoke you in his name! You and your hurricane-spirits that pass through the atmosphere at tremendous speeds must obey my orders. I invoke you, king of the demonic spirits of the air! Appear visibly here before my circle and confirm the reception of my request. Do not hesitate, for if you do, I will torture and torment you in your master's name! King of the air, appear before me now!"

Amidst ear-splitting howls, an air spirit became visible in the magic triangle.

"You earthworm! If you were not our most supreme lord's ally, I would tear you to pieces with my element. You dare threaten me in such a manner? It is only due to your pact that I owe you my obedience. Now, express your request!"

"I demand the destruction of Frabato," the Grand Master called out authoritatively. "Your spirits of the air shall persecute him continuously and thwart his every deed. Make him a powerless weakling."

"I will do what is within my power, but I cannot promise success, for the Brothers of Light are behind Frabato," the king of the air replied scornfully — and then he too disappeared.

The mention of Frabato's special position, his power and the source of his protection, caused hatred and rage to surge anew in the Grand Master's soul. In such a mood he turned westward:

"Forces of water, I conjure you! Listen to my demand, beings of the watery element! Mighty demon prince of the waters, I invoke you. I am linked with your element and I speak your language. I call you in the name of Satan, your lord. I, the ally of your ruler, must be obeyed at once; ascend from the roaring ocean and appear visibly here before my circle to confirm the reception of my requests. Do not refuse to come or I shall persecute you in your infernal ruler's name with the element of fire! Prince of the waters, appear to me!"

With an immense roar, a peculiar being, half human and half fish, materialized in the magic triangle and addressed the magician in a hoarse voice:

"You have called me from my element, even though you know that I detest large cities. If you were not my master's ally I would have you plagued by my element because of your threats. Now, tell me what you want and do it quickly!"

Seething with anger and hate, the Grand Master cried out, "I have not called you from the depths of the sea without reason. In the name of your lord and master, I demand the persecution and destruction of Frabato. He is the first to resist our lodge, and therefore I want him exterminated!"

"I will try to fulfill your wish. What is in my power will be done, but success cannot be guaranteed. Much will depend on whether we can seize Frabato in a weak hour."

The magician dismissed the being with his magic wand; it vanished.

He was enraged that the princes of the elements had not promised him full success; he began to realize the great difficulties that were to come. In order to complete his magic square, he had to invoke the prince of the earth element as well. He faced north.

"Mighty prince of the hellish element of earth, your master's ally is calling you in his name. In the name of Satan, leave the underworld and appear visibly before my circle and confirm to me that you have received my request. Obey my commands immediately, otherwise I will torment you in the name of your master. Prince of the earth, appear to me now!"

The ground beneath the Grand Master's feet quaked and, with a crashing roar, a small man with gray hair and a long chin appeared in the magic triangle. His large, dark, deep-set eyes flashed at the black magician. In his right hand he held a lantern which emitted a light that was strangely dim and yet intense. The earth spirit stared at the magician with a penetrating look and said:

"Reluctantly I have left my realm to obey your will. According to the spiritual laws and by virtue of your pact I owe you obedience until you die. What is your wish?"

The deep voice and the powerfully icy stare of the being caused a cold shudder to run down the magician's spine. It suddenly occurred to him that at his death he would become a servant to this creature.

The prince of gnomes waited quietly in the magic triangle. He could read the magician's thoughts and feelings quite easily, and it seemed to fill him with great pleasure that this power-mad man would be his subject in the future.

Though almost paralyzed, the Grand Master composed himself, saying, "I know what is in store for me; but in the present I cannot remain inactive and watch an outsider celebrate his success and ridicule our lodge. I therefore demand that you persecute and destroy Frabato with all your powers. Pull him down into the depths of your realm and surround him with a veil of darkness so that he cannot escape. This is my will! The extermination of Frabato will serve the image of your master and our brotherhood."

"I will do what is in my power," answered the spirit of earth softly, "but I cannot guarantee full success in the case of a man like Frabato."

The earth spirit disappeared and the entire building suddenly became as silent as a graveyard. The invocation of the elemental beings had so exhausted the Grand Master that

46

he stood in the magic circle as if physically beaten. He was breathing heavily and an emptiness pervaded his mind. He saw the demon spirit which served him every day standing in a corner of the room. This entity had been at his side for many years, helping him fulfill his wishes; he had become completely dependent upon the creature. He was aware that he no longer had the power to loosen himself from his chains; the spiritual laws gave him no chance to annul his pact with the rulers of demonic powers. The power which he had gained through his pact would not last forever, and, just as he was a master today, he would be a slave tomorrow. He had been unable to satisfy his lust for material power and wealth with his occult abilities; therefore he had succumbed to the temptation of a magical pact. A feeling of dependency weighed upon him like a nightmare in this very hour; he suffered hellish torments he had never before experienced in his life. His hatred for Frabato was immense, though, and it was fueled by the failure of the princes of the four elements to guarantee him success.

The question, "What powerful authority is behind this Frabato?" hammered in his mind. "I want him destroyed even if I have to risk my own life!"

Driven by these thoughts, the Grand Master decided to invoke the master of demonic powers himself, and ask him to fulfill his wish. The black magician laid his sword upon the floor inside the circle and placed his left foot upon it. He raised the magic wand with his right hand and drew the seal of darkness in the air, the agreed-upon sign which would invoke the very master of demons.

He had scarcely completed the seal when a glaring ray ascended from the ground and illumined the entire room. The Grand Master stood there as if struck by lightning and struggled to retain consciousness, for the room had been filled with a deadly paralyzing vibration. No ordinary mortal would have been able to survive this terrible energy, and only the Grand Master's pact saved him from instant annihilation.

A very peculiar figure slowly condensed in the triangle, sporting the horned head of a he-goat and a hairy human body with breasts. Its hands had freakish, talon-like fingers, and its feet were like the hooves of a bull. A long, thick tail completed the figure.

After the apparition became completely visible, the ray of light disappeared into the ground. Only rarely had the magician seen this spirit, for this was Baphomet himself, the master of demons!

Baphomet spoke sneeringly to the trembling Grand Master:

"Well, great magician, I know of your wish to destroy Frabato. It is a good idea and I will support it with all my power. However, it will not be easy, for this Frabato is a man with a special spiritual mission. This is why our proven methods have failed thus far. If you insist on your request, we face a difficult task. Perhaps you should spend the rest of your days enjoying other pleasures in life."

A battle raged between the Grand Master's conscience, his fear, and his hate. In the end his hatred was victorious and in a blind rage he mumbled, "What have I made this pact for? You are obligated to assist me until the end of my life. You may triumph over me after my death, but now I demand your assistance in the extermination of Frabato. I shall have no pleasure in life otherwise. May he be eternally damned!"

After the magician had uttered his curse, the uncanny visitor vanished into the ground without replying. The paralyzing tension dissolved at once. Completely exhausted, the Grand Master uttered the dismissal formula for all the beings he had invoked, whilst adding a few protective formulas just to be sure. He hurriedly locked all the magical aids in their respective cabinets and left the temple.

He fell onto a sofa in an adjacent room, unable for some

time to formulate a clear thought. After a cup of strong coffee he felt somewhat revived, but he was unable to cast off the dramatic events of the day.

The sun was shining brightly in the blue sky, but the Grand Master was sullen as he left the lodge and hastily made his way home.

Chapter V

On the evening of that same day, the lecture room of the Eccentric Club was sold out. Frabato was giving a private seance for reporters and scientists, and only invited guests were permitted. There were, however, some F.O.G.C. members among those present, for the lodge had its representatives among every social class.

When the session was over, the reporters surrounded Frabato, plaguing him with questions. After their first onslaught, and when their curiosity had been sufficiently satisfied, Frabato withdrew into a separate room for further discussion with a smaller group. When the subject of hypnosis was raised, Frabato explained with regret that he would henceforth be unable to perform hypnotic demonstrations upon members of his audience. A police inspector had informed him of a new law regarding hypnosis; Frabato had promised to obey it.

The new law caused a sudden stirring in the group. A reporter shouted to Frabato, "I will wager five hundred marks that you will not dare to carry out a demonstration of hypnosis in your next performance!"

Frabato felt cornered. It was not his practice to transgress against civil law. On the other hand, it was beneath his dignity to allow himself to be called a coward — especially as he had been strongly harassed by the devotees of sensationalism. Confident that some saving idea would occur to him, he accepted the wager.

He left the club soon afterwards and drove back to the hotel in his car.

Next morning, he reflected once more on the events of the previous day. He became suspicious that the wager was in fact an attempt at entrapment by the F.O.G.C. Lodge. Suddenly, he had a good idea how to evade the trap without losing the wager.

He dressed quickly and went for a walk, perfecting each detail of his plan. After breakfast he posted his mail and then drove into the city.

He entered a large music shop on Wilhelmstrasse and asked a saleswoman whether it were possible to record his voice and then take the disc with him immediately thereafter. The woman said yes and took Frabato to the studio.

Frabato did not leave the music shop till afternoon. Heavily laden with a number of records, he merrily made his way back to the hotel.

*

The grand hall in the art gallery was lively. Reporters from the Dresden papers were anxious not to miss the evening. A steady stream of people pushed its way into the already crowded hall to witness the demonstrations of the mysterious Frabato.

Smiling, Frabato appeared on the stage. After the welcoming applause had subsided, he addressed the audience:

"Ladies and gentlemen, I thank you very much for such a warm welcome, and for your great interest in my performances. In one of my former lectures I pointed out that there are many things between heaven and earth which ordinary mortals cannot easily understand or master. I was permitted to present you with evidence of the power of magnetism, the influence of the human will over any distance, and of clairvoyance and telepathy.

"As in previous performances, I would like to ask you once again to assist me in my demonstrations. To begin with, I want to introduce you to the world of the departed, and to show you that man's existence does not end with what we call death; on the contrary, true life begins. Life in the physical body is to be regarded as a sort of preparation for this.

"I will refrain from turning tables and the like, as these are the methods traditionally employed by charlatans. I do hope to provide you with a more impressive show by calling some of the spirits of the dead to this stage."

A murmur rushed throughout the hall after Frabato's astonishing proclamation, finally giving way to an expectant silence when a gentleman left his seat and stepped onto the stage.

"My name is Schneider," he said, introducing himself to Frabato, "and I am a professor of chemistry. You are talking, and quite convincingly, about spiritual powers and entities whose existence is, at this time, denied by orthodox science. I would be grateful to you if you could give me any evidence of the spiritual powers you describe. Being a scientist and a skeptic, I shall not be easily convinced."

Frabato asked the audience whether he had their permission to address the professor's question with the relevant evidence. The answer was a unanimous "yes" and an enthusiastic round of applause. Everyone was eager and curious to learn what sort of experiment Frabato would perform in order to convince the skeptic.

Frabato offered the professor a seat at the edge of the stage and asked him to be patient for a few moments; he wanted to say a few words about the teachings of spiritualism first. He had spoken only a few sentences, however, when there was a sudden visible change in the professor. The man became quite obviously pale; his eyes stared into space. Then he slipped from his chair, fell in a heap, and lay motionless.

Some members of the audience cried out. Others rose from their seats, craning their necks to see what had happened.

Throughout the commotion, Frabato did not bat an eyelid.

He did not even look at the professor. Eventually, he raised his hand and asked for silence, saying:

"Ladies and gentlemen, please remain quiet. No harm will come to the professor. To surprise you, I have detached a portion of my personality during the course of my lecture and sent it to extract the greater part of the professor's astral vitality. By so doing, I have induced in him a state similar to that of death. He is no longer breathing and his heartbeat has ceased. A medical diagnosis would probably be heart failure."

Frabato was thinking of the F.O.G.C. brethren, some of whom were certainly present. They would be seething inwardly, for here he was publicly demonstrating that heart failure could be caused by occult means.

Frabato then turned towards the professor, placed his feet together and propped him up like a rigid wooden marionette. Two assistants then laid him across two chairs which had been placed sufficiently far apart so that his body was supported solely by his neck and heels.

After a blanket had been placed over the professor, Frabato stepped onto a chair and then onto the professor's abdomen. He asked his assistants to join him; now there were three people standing on the professor's motionless body which bore the weight of the three men as if made of steel.

After the three of them stepped down, the tension in the audience exploded into applause. At a signal from Frabato, the assistants brought the professor to his feet again and supported him with their arms.

The magician now asked for silence and stared into one of the far corners of the stage. Almost unnoticed by the audience, the professor's appearance underwent yet another complete transformation. The mask-like rigidity of his face disappeared; he started breathing again and his cheeks flushed with color. Frabato faced the professor, who, after Frabato had focused his gaze upon him for a short time, began to breathe freely and blink his eyelids.

As though awakening from a deep sleep, he stretched his limbs and looked at his surroundings in astonishment. But it was not until he caught sight of Frabato that he was restored to full consciousness.

Frabato smiled at him, saying, "Well, professor, I am most certain that you could tell the audience a very interesting story about your experiences."

As he was still a bit shaky on his legs, the professor seated himself on a chair with the help of an assistant. Frabato looked intently at him again for a few seconds, thus restoring him to the state in which he had first taken the stage. The professor rose, pushed the chair aside, and shook Frabato's hand with enthusiasm.

"I was not expecting anything like that! I shall remember this event until the end of my days. But I am still completely at a loss as to how you could influence me to such a degree during your performance."

With a laugh, Frabato answered. "This ability is the result of many years worth of meditation and training. You have experienced for yourself how effective it is. But you really should not keep the audience waiting any longer for your report."

"As I was attentively listening to Frabato's words," the professor began, "I did not notice at all that I was under any foreign influence. But suddenly I felt that my head was completely empty and that I was unable to move. To my horror, I saw my body fall to the floor of the stage in front of me. The feeling of rigidity soon left me and gave way to a sensation of tranquility, freedom and lightness which I have never experienced before. I was able to move about the stage freely, connected to my body solely by a fine silvery thread. In that manner, I was able to witness what Frabato and his assistants did with my body, and I was extremely relieved when it survived the experiment without harm. During the experiment, one of the assistants walked right through me in a very remarkable way, and I noticed I had no shadow on the stage, despite the fact that I felt like a physical being. After the assistants had propped my body up again, Frabato looked at me with his penetrating eyes and I moved towards my body as if attracted by a powerful magnet. Although I tried to resist this force, my efforts were in vain and I lost consciousness. When I awoke, I found myself back in my physical body.

"There is no longer any doubt in my mind that the human spirit survives the death of the physical body, and that this spirit moves in the way described by Frabato in his lecture."

Having rendered Frabato his exuberant thanks, the professor returned to his seat, accompanied by delighted applause. An expectant silence spread again, and Frabato continued:

"Ladies and gentlemen, I am very pleased that the professor, as a neutral party, has confirmed the existence of the human spirit independent of the physical body. I should like to mention that an individual without any training in magic will, after his death, be unable to perceive any sensory impressions from the physical world. I should like to stress that experiments like these should never be attempted by the layman. For if the operator lacks complete power over the elements, the harmony of spirit, soul, and body may remain disturbed and the volunteer end up in a mental institution. Let this be a warning!

"But now let us turn our attention to further experiments. Who among you would like to contact a deceased acquaintance or relative?"

At first, no one was courageous enough to break the suspense with a response to Frabato's question. Finally, a gentleman volunteered for the experiment; the audience gave him their relieved applause. Once on stage, he introduced himself as Mr. Müller and said that he was the director of a bank. Rather emotionally, he said he wished to see his deceased sister and learn something of her present fate.

In order to put the man at ease, Frabato asked him to be seated in a chair on the stage, saying, "Please tell me the name of the deceased and the date she died."

"Her name was Elisabeth Müller, and she died on May 16th, 1929, in the local sanatorium."

Frabato asked the audience if anyone else had known this person, whereupon an elderly woman in Mr. Müller's row quickly rose and identified herself as the mother of the deceased. Two men from the same row said that they, too, were relatives of the deceased, and a woman from the audience said that Elisabeth Müller had been her friend and schoolmate.

"That is enough," said Frabato. "I prefer to have a number of people who can identify the deceased individual upon whom I call. And now I kindly ask for your attention."

Frabato sat in a corner of the stage so that he could be seen by everyone. His movements were greeted with a sense of silent expectation from the audience. A few moments passed; the magician became pale and rigid. In time his color returned, but his face had changed so dramatically that it no longer bore any resemblance to that of Frabato.

The deceased's mother cried out, "Liese!"

Frabato stood up gracefully. His elegant movements and his transformed features were those of a young woman. Clearly, he had loaned his own body to the dead woman's spirit so that she could speak to her brother.

Director Müller, who had recognized his sister's movements and features, was trembling all over. He shook his head as if unable to believe his senses, until the familiar soft voice of his sister spoke through Frabato's body.

"Willi, I never thought I would be able to speak to you again. How is our family? I know our father has died, for I am in contact with him often."

Spellbound, the director stared at Frabato, through whom

his deceased sister was actually speaking. "She" took a chair and sat down near him; they had a short conversation about private matters, then she asked for a pencil and paper with which to write a note to Robert, her former fiancé. She gave the note to her brother and asked him to give her love to all of her relatives. After saying good-bye, she shook hands with him and then sat down in the corner chair again. Frabato's body went rigid once more, as at the beginning of the experiment. After a few seconds the rigidity gave way and Frabato's familiar features returned.

Frabato now rose and turned to the teary-eyed bank director who was studying the note in his hand.

"Impossible. And yet possible," he whispered. "And it truly is my sister's handwriting."

"I hope you are now convinced that your sister still exists. Or do you doubt that she has just spoken to you through me?"

"No, I am no longer in doubt," Mr. Müller answered. "And I thank you from the bottom of my heart for your mediation."

Still bewildered by his miraculous experience, Mr. Müller left the stage and returned to his seat.

Frabato declared the first part of the performance at an end and promised a few humorous scenes after intermission.

*

Accompanied by applause, Frabato reappeared on stage after the intermission.

"Ladies and gentlemen," he began, "In my previous performance I promised to show you a few examples of suggestion and hypnosis. Unfortunately, the practice of hypnosis is now forbidden by the police. This is rather untimely, but I have made some preparations to entertain and amuse you through other means.

"I shall now leave the hall for approximately half an hour. If two people from the audience would kindly accompany me to the refreshment room, I will then have reliable witnesses later on. Enjoy the program!"

A policeman and a gentleman from the audience volunteered to go with Frabato. The three made their way to the lounge.

A certain anticipation spread throughout the hall, and all eyes were focused on the stage; everyone was convinced that Frabato must have left something interesting behind. And they were not mistaken, for they suddenly heard his voice come forth over the loudspeaker.

"Ladies and gentlemen, although I am not in the hall, my spirit is still with you, for we do not want to interrupt the performance. Please follow my instructions exactly.

"Look to the center of the stage without interruption, as though I were there personally. Those who can do so will be able to envision my person there. Now I am spreading an invisible fluid over everyone present, which will bring about complete tranquility and harmony.

"You are so quiet now that it even makes you tired. Your fatigue is increasing constantly, as if you had been doing heavy work. With every breath you become more and more tired. The desire for sleep dominates your thinking altogether. Your eyelids are closing and you are now in a deep, dreamless sleep. Your sleep is so deep that nothing can awaken you. No noise can disturb you or awaken you. You will awaken only when I give the command.

"Those ladies and gentlemen who have not fallen asleep should now clap their hands loudly, whistle or shout to try and awaken their sleeping neighbors. But they will not succeed!"

Many in the audience had fallen into a deep sleep; the hall became quite noisy as those who were still awake tried in any number of ways to wake up the sleeping people.

However, this proved to be impossible. A few minutes later, Frabato's voice was heard again.

"Even if you were shooting off cannons, you would be unable to awaken the sleeping, for they are in a state of deep trance and will respond only to my specific orders.

"I am now gathering all you sleepers under my will power. You will listen only to my words and do precisely as I say. After I count to three, everyone will awaken. You will feel refreshed and healthy, and you will be unable to remember what transpired.

"One! Weariness and drowsiness are fading, contentment and happiness fill your whole being.

"Two! Your health is strengthened. You feel extremely well and all unpleasantness has vanished.

"Three! Everyone awake!"

Upon awakening, all those who had slept looked around in astonishment at the general merriment in the hall; they could not believe they had been so fast asleep. But before a detailed explanation could take place, the voice from the loudspeaker asked ten ladies and ten gentlemen to take seats on the chairs which had been arranged onstage. They were to sit in pairs, a gentleman next to a lady. After some minor confusion the volunteers managed to seat themselves correctly, and Frabato gave further instructions.

"Ladies and gentlemen on the stage, you will now listen to music. A waltz will be played for you. You will feel an urge to dance with one another. Each of the gentlemen on the stage will dance with the woman on his right. Nothing will disturb you, for there is an invisible wall between the audience and the stage and you are not able to see the spectators."

Although no music was heard, some pairs engaged themselves in a formal dance, spinning round to the rhythm of a waltz. Other pairs moved more comically, and the audience laughed. But it did not seem to disturb the dancers in the least.

"Stop!" the voice said from the loudspeaker. "The dance has ended. The ladies and gentlemen on the stage will be served some refreshments before saying goodbye to one another. There is a basket with apples, pears and peaches at the edge of the stage and you may serve yourselves. You will wake up immediately after the first bite without having swallowed anything, and you will return to your seats in the hall with a feeling of happiness. Please come for me and my escorts in the refreshment room now."

The hypnotized people on the stage reached out for the putative fruit. But as soon as they had taken a bite, they awoke and, with sour expressions on their faces, began to grumble. "Damn, this is not a peach at all. It is an onion!" one of the afflicted said with tears in his eyes. Someone else said, "Yuck! This is a raw potato!" The surprises continued.

After the last person had left the stage, a spectator went to the refreshment room to bring back Frabato and his escorts.

Greeted by applause, Frabato stepped onto the stage and addressed the audience with a smile. "I can tell from your faces that you have enjoyed yourselves. I am pleased that you have liked this part of the performance too, although I myself was not present in the hall. I am deeply indebted to my two excellent witnesses. This is the end of today's program. All of you are invited to my next performance, which will take place the day after tomorrow. Good night to you all."

As the curtain slowly fell, Frabato went to his dressing room. He had just changed his clothes when two gentlemen entered unannounced.

"You are Frabato, are you not?" one of the men asked.

When Frabato nodded, the man produced his identification. "Criminal Police. You are under arrest. Please, come along with us."

A waiting car took them to the police station where Frabato was taken into custody.

*

On the following day, the newspapers featured a detailed report of Frabato's sensational experiments and his arrest by the police. Early the same morning Frabato was taken to the chief of police, who was clearly annoyed and launched an immediate verbal attack upon him.

"You have violated the new law and continued to experiment with hypnosis. Witnesses report that more than a hundred people were hypnotized. You will have to pay dearly for this. And it will not go easy for you in court."

The chief was furious, pacing up and down the room nervously.

"This is so shameful," he exploded again. "Did you have to do it here, of all places? What kind of a public image do *I* have now?"

Frabato sat without saying a word and allowed the chief of police to vent his frustration; he only began to speak when he saw the other man's anger subsiding.

"You have certainly been given false information, for I did not hypnotize anyone yesterday," Frabato replied. "One of your own officers can bear witness to the fact that I was in the refreshment room at the time in question. The audience spent half an hour with my phonograph records, it is true, but I can scarcely be held responsible for that: after all, there was nothing to prevent your officers from turning off the record player. Since I was not present in the hall personally, I do not feel the least bit guilty."

The chief looked at Frabato suspiciously, then called for the officer who had accompanied Frabato to the refreshment room. He confirmed Frabato's account. The chief was satisfied and shook hands with Frabato, saying:

"You should have become a diplomat instead of a magician. You certainly have a knack for looking at matters from a different perspective. You are free to go, and I apologize for the zeal of my people."

Frabato said goodbye and went back to his hotel at once. He needed a good rest, for his night in jail had not been especially comfortable.

The next day the newspapers reported Frabato's release, together with the announcement that his next performance would take place that evening as scheduled.

Chapter VI

The Grand Master of the F.O.G.C. Lodge was the owner of a very beautiful villa in the city's most elegant district, exquisitely furnished and surrounded by a well-tended garden. He was highly regarded in business circles, a great man in his profession with an enormous financial income.

But today he sat gloomily behind his desk at home, playing distractedly with a golden fountain pen. He was in the grips of an unrest which could not be soothed even by his harmonious surroundings.

He got up and began pacing the room thoughtfully. His servants were under strict orders not to disturb him or admit any visitors.

For the first time in many years, the chain of his success had been broken. Until now, all his plans had been carried out successfully, but Frabato was a difficult matter which weighed heavily on his soul. He felt somehow that there was a much greater power behind this mysterious man than that which lay behind his own lodge, whose members were only able to realize their plans with the assistance of negative forces.

A man more powerful than he! The idea fed the Grand Master's inexorable hatred, incessantly driving him to seek to persecute and harm Frabato by whatever means.

And though it was difficult for him, he had to admit that Frabato had foiled all his attacks. No one had ever violated the laws of the lodge, been punished for it, and escaped to tell the tale. And all those who had been sentenced to death by the tepaphone had, until now, been destroyed.

Every person has a weak point where he can be easily wounded. The Grand Master had been looking in vain for a weakness in Frabato; his failure to discover one overwhelmed him with hatred and rage. He had already been informed that the police action against Frabato for breach of the prohibition on hypnosis had been ineffective. This new failure heightened his ill-temper; thoughts of revenge flashed through his mind. Under ordinary circumstances he was a master of self-control, but now his face mirrored just how badly his nerves had suffered from recent events. Even the ticking of his exquisite clock provoked his uneasiness, mixed with a feeling of fear and horror that he had never experienced before.

The Grand Master had been nourishing his dark thoughts for a long time when he came up with what he thought was a good idea. He sat down at his desk and wrote a letter to a government official who was also a member of the F.O.G.C. Lodge.

Dear brother and supporter:

As you know, Frabato has thwarted many of our plans. We have tried in vain to make him a member of our lodge and to convince him of our goodwill. Because of his magical abilities, he has been able to discover all our lodge's secrets. He not only knows our initiation rites, but is also well versed in our most secret plans. These facts clearly show that this man remains a permanent danger to our lodge.

As you also know, we have not yet been able to eliminate him. Even the tepaphone failed, and our allied King of Demons has been unable to guarantee success.

With his magical abilities, this Frabato naturally has access to the most secret plans of the government and the military as well. If a hostile government were to succeed in employing him as a spy, immeasurable damage could

66

be done to you, dear brother, as well as to the entire nation. As my own means are now exhausted, I here request your assistance in annihilating this dangerous man. The brotherhood is greatly interested in settling this matter and I hope that you will not disappoint me.

I look forward to consulting with you personally and remain:

Yours faithfully,
S.

The Grand Master placed the letter in an envelope, pressed the lodge's insignia into the sealing wax, then called his servant and ordered him to take the letter to the post office at once.

Now his countenance reflected delight, and he rubbed his hands together in satisfaction. He was convinced that this plan could be carried out successfully, for political dissidents were dealt with quickly in those days. The secret police would see to the matter.

The recent events had strongly affected the Grand Master's health. He had lost a lot of weight and his hands trembled. His unresolved problems had placed him in a constant state of agitation, and he felt that he had aged.

Quite involuntarily, he stepped in front of a large mirror. As he thoughtlessly studied his reflection, he noticed, with increasing terror, that a phosphorescent glow had suddenly appeared between his eyebrows. With wide eyes he stared at his own trembling image, for he was fully aware of the meaning of this sign. It was known to the lodge as the sign of death.

Paralyzed with shock, the Grand Master was unable to avert his eyes from the flame which gradually became bigger, eventually covering the entire surface of the mirror. Behind the flame a grotesque face with penetrating eyes slowly appeared, and an inner voice spoke as if from the depths of a grave:

"Brother, your last hour is near!"

The Grand Master was now perspiring profusely, and he felt surrounded by an icy coldness.

Slowly, the demon's face faded away and the flame dwindled, the mirror finally reflecting only the ash-gray face of the black magician.

Although he still felt paralyzed, he managed to tear himself away from his image in the mirror, fall into a chair, and stay there for some time, quite motionless. He cradled his head in his hands despairingly.

"This damned Frabato," he murmured. "I must not think of him anymore or else I shall go mad!"

The Grand Master energetically chased away his negative thoughts, lit a cigar and walked up and down his study, trying to calm himself. It occurred to him that he had yet more aggravation in store today. The astrological position of the Sun reminded him, however, that he would soon have to set forth, for it was the twenty-third of June, the day of the lodge's general meeting. It was important that he, as the president, should appear calm and collected in order to set an example for the other brethren.

He ordered his servant to prepare his supper. At the end of the meal he drank a cup of strong coffee, changed his clothes and ordered his driver to take him to the lodge buildings.

*

The twenty-third of June is a special day of the year for people all over the world; it is then that the sun reaches its highest point, the longest day and shortest night of the year.

To celebrate the summer solstice, many European peoples

68

have traditionally lit a great bonfire. The Brothers of Light, especially those of the lower degrees, carry out the so-called St. John's evocations on this particular night. During this rite, as many as three wishes may be sent into the invisible astral world. These wishes are then fulfilled during the coming year, as long as they do not violate the laws of karma. This ritual of the St. John's Mystery is a strictly kept secret among the Brothers of the Light.

Although the twenty-third of June was also a special day for the F.O.G.C. Lodge, it was by no means a happy one for them. Quite the contrary: it was a fatal day, for one of the lodge's brethren must sacrifice his life to the demon he served. All members, regardless of rank or grade, were subject to this law.

The lodge has ninety-nine members. The hundredth member is the demon who presides over the lodge and who, in turn, delegates a subordinate demon to each lodge member for the realization of that member's wishes. Each demon has its own special name and sign of invocation known only to the lodge brother it serves. The demon's name and sign are never entrusted to anyone else; the penalty for breaking silence is death.

The sacrificial victim is chosen by lot. A new member is then admitted to replace the victim and the demon of his predecessor is normally allotted to him. With ill luck, a new member might be put to death in his very first year.

It was not surprising that the lodge members, by virtue of this exchange, were enabled to pursue solid material goals and were wealthy and influential people. Someone from the lower or poorer classes was only admitted to the membership if he possessed special talents and abilities that could serve the purposes of the lodge. Large sums of money were immediately placed at the disposal of such a member, until, with the help of his demon, he had learned to stand on his own feet.

The summer weather was marvelous on this particular June 23rd. The warm, still air of the day lingered over the countryside, but fear hovered like an invisible cloud in the minds of the F.O.G.C. brethren. Only at this time every year did they choose to remember that sacrifice hung like Damocles' sword over their heads.

The great hall of the lodge house was ceremoniously illuminated. There were ninety-eight numbered chairs standing on a small platform facing the Grand Master's place. Each member of the lodge had received a number and had to take his seat accordingly. No one was permitted to be absent from this most important meeting of the year. Each brother was expected to arrange his private affairs in such a way as to allow him to be present that evening.

Although the meeting was to commence at 8:00 P.M., most of the members had already gathered by 7:30 and were talking animatedly to one another in small groups. As the minute hand of the clock moved inexorably towards the appointed hour, the lodge brethren took their seats on the numbered chairs. The Vice President, who was also the Secretary, had already taken his seat.

Precisely at eight o'clock, the Grand Master entered the hall. Everyone rose silently to greet their superior. The Grand Master, still in shock due to the events of the afternoon, gathered his strength and opened the meeting by striking a large gong three times with a special mallet, its sound resonating throughout the hall. Then he addressed the brethren:

"My dear brothers, I thank you for your welcome and ask that you be seated. I am very pleased that you have all come. As you know, today is an historic and traditional day for our lodge, for one of our members must leave us and another must be admitted. Only after we have drawn lots will we know who is to go. I realize that you are anticipating the balloting with dread; however, you were told during your admission to the lodge that the procedure is written in our regulations and is compulsory.

"Our order has existed for many centuries and is represented throughout the world with the same laws. Ninety-nine is a holy number for us and has a special meaning, for there are ninety-nine of our lodges in the world and each of these lodges again has exactly ninety-nine members. All these lodges adhere to the same laws as we do. The Master of Darkness, our god, whom we honor and worship, has provided each lodge with a demonic entity of high rank. This presiding entity is obliged to provide a demon servant for each lodge brother. Since the Grand Master of each lodge is to carry the greatest responsibility, the presiding entity is assigned to him.

"On this historic day I should like to remind each of you of the enormous advantages you have obtained by becoming members of our lodge. I am certain that not one of you can name an Order in which riches and power can be gained more quickly. Who can destroy his enemies quicker than we? Who is better protected against all of life's dangers than our own brethren? No one! These advantages can only be achieved with the support of the spiritual forces of whom I have just spoken. We have all chosen these advantages for ourselves and, in return, we are required to support evil and fight against good wherever possible. Surely none of you have ever found this to be terribly difficult. The greatest risk in all of this is the present evening's event — but your chances of remaining in the lodge are great.

"Nonetheless, I am fully convinced, my dear brothers, that none of you has ever regretted taking this step, that each of you is financially affluent, and that you have been able to realize your goals with the assistance of your spiritual servant."

The Grand Master interrupted his speech to observe the effect of his words on the other brethren. Many expressed their satisfaction with a slight nod.

The Grand Master drank some water and was about to continue praising the advantages of the lodge when he suddenly remembered his unsuccessful battle against Frabato. Rage consumed him and, controlling himself with great effort, he continued:

"Fellow members, as you know, a powerful enemy has been trying to oppose our lodge's aims. It is the magician Frabato. Unfortunately, our attacks against him have thus far been unsuccessful, and he has even been able to defend himself against the tepaphone. I therefore encourage you to remain united in this matter. This man can be dangerous to all of us, and we must adhere to the slogan: 'All for one and one for all!'"

The Grand Master was almost in a state of ecstasy now, but many of the members remained reserved, not wishing to interfere in his personal vendetta. Others felt shivers run down their spines; there was fear in their faces. It became clear to many that here was a man whose might was greater than that of the lodge. Who had ever resisted the tepaphone, the instrument which could bring death to anyone, no matter where on earth he might be? The Grand Master must have a special reason to deal with this matter personally, or even to discuss his difficulties with the brotherhood. The thought of such a powerful enemy caused extreme uneasiness among the brethren. This was all clear to the Grand Master when he cried out with triumphant and scornful laughter:

"As I can see, many of you have become terribly frightened at the mere mention of Frabato's name. It should not remain a secret to you that this man has caused me many distressing hours.

"But our lodge has many ways to annihilate such an enemy; you all know that the Master of Darkness is at my side whenever I have need of his assistance and advice. You may therefore rest assured, my dear brothers, that, thanks to my advantageous connections, I have been able to cast suspicion on Frabato on political grounds. I do know, of course, that he is in no way politically engaged, but in spite of this it will take no longer than a week before he is incarcerated. From there it is only one short step to his death, for with the right amount of money it is easy to find people who will aid in such a task. At any rate, I can promise you that soon Frabato will no longer be among the living!"

The Grand Master's last words caused a sigh of relief, for Frabato was already a nightmare to many of the lodge members. The Grand Master realized with satisfaction that the unity of the lodge had been restored. Relieved, he gave the chair to the Secretary and sat down.

The Secretary thanked the Grand Master for his speech, then addressed the assembly:

"My dear brothers, as you know, today you are to submit your reports, written in secret code and covering the work accomplished during the past year with the help of your demon servant. This allows us a certain amount of control in examining whether the conditions of our contract with the demonic powers have been met. Those of you who have had specific problems or difficulties with your spirit servants may discuss the matter with the Grand Master after tonight's meeting. He will then clear the matter with the relevant spiritual entity. Now, my dear brothers, I ask you to give me your reports, and I remind you once again that your report must be marked with your allotted number."

Two of the members were asked to gather the papers and submit them to the Secretary, who counted and examined them carefully.

There was a richly ornamented cabinet behind the Grand Master's chair and, moving slowly (as if wanting to stop time), the Secretary locked the reports in the drawer, opened another drawer, removed a wooden chest and set it on the table next to the cabinet. Then, quite serious, he faced the assembly and opened the fateful box. It contained ninety-nine small envelopes. Concealed therein were the members' numbers, which would determine the fate of one of them. An oppressive silence took hold of the assembly, for this was the darkest and most terrible hour of the year for each and every one of them.

The Secretary now obtained a drum from an adjacent room. This was mounted on a frame which enabled it to be turned round its axle by a handle. It was placed in the center of the hall by the Secretary, who then opened a small door on its side. After setting Brother Silesius' number aside, he solemnly dropped one envelope after the other into the drum under the watchful eyes of the brethren. When he was finished, he closed the door to the drum.

One of the lodge brethren escorted the caretaker's daughter into the room. Elli knew what she had to do, for she had performed this same service on St. John's Eve for many years. She knew absolutely nothing of the true seriousness of the hour; she had always been satisfied with the explanation that a member was to be chosen for a "special mission." The generous sum of money she received for this small task quelled any further curiosity — and she knew quite well that too much curiosity on her part could result in her father losing his position.

The Secretary blindfolded the young lady and led her carefully to the drum. Then he took the handle and spun the drum, ten turns to the left and ten to the right. Then he opened the lid, led Elli's hand above it, and asked her to pull out an envelope. Without hesitation, Elli extracted an envelope which the Secretary took from her and laid on the table for everyone to see.

Forcing himself to remain calm, the Secretary removed the blindfold from Elli's eyes, gave her her customary gratuity and accompanied her out of the building with a few friendly words. He then returned to the hall, where the brethren were waiting for him with pale faces. He reached for the fateful envelope and pulled out the number.

In a loud and trembling voice he said: "It is Number One, the number of our Grand Master!"

The tension was released, though with varied reactions. Some members began, with excitation, to discuss the result, while others simply remained silent, chins propped on their hands.

The Grand Master, who had been standing, carefully observing the entire procedure, fell into his chair, deathly pale. Muttering unintelligibly, he stared at the ceiling. A demon's grimace took shape before his inner vision. A death sweat poured from his forehead and he called out in despair, "Frabato!"

The Grand Master's reaction filled the special gathering with an uncanny horror, for never before had anyone faced his death in such a cowardly manner. Although all the sacrificial victims had been hit hard by their fate, they had made a great effort to retain, at least externally, some degree of composure. In contrast, the Grand Master, who should have been an example for the whole lodge, was a pitiful sight. It took some time before he could regain his self-control.

Finally, his facial muscles twitching visibly, he addressed the assembly in a broken voice:

"My dear brothers, as you all know, I have recently been struggling with the case of Frabato. I have attempted to annihilate him in several ways but have not yet succeeded. As I have told you, he even survived the tepaphone, our most powerful weapon. It may be concluded from this that Frabato is allied with powerful forces. Because I am Frabato's greatest enemy, there is no doubt in my mind that he influenced this draw with his magical powers and arranged matters so that my number would be drawn. Many of you were present at his public demonstrations, where he proved his influence over people, and his ability to make them compliant to his will from any distance."

The Grand Master stopped and looked around expectantly. Many approved by nodding their heads, for they had witnessed the demonstrations. When the Grand Master noticed that these individuals seemed sympathetic towards him, he was encouraged to go on, saying: "My dear brothers, please consider that I am the only one among you who has unremittingly tried to annihilate this enemy. Therefore, I declare that he has influenced Elli to draw my number from the drum. For this reason I cannot acknowledge the draw!"

With these words, a subdued grumble spread through the hall, for everyone would willingly have foregone another draw. The lodge brethren knew that cowardice and mortal fear had driven their Grand Master to take this step; however, it was impossible to contradict him openly, for it was laid down in the lodge's laws that the Grand Master could twice demand another draw if he so wished. This was something that rarely ever happened and, in all ninety-nine lodges combined, had only occurred twice during the last two centuries.

Having been marked as a candidate for death, the Grand Master was required to forfeit his right to govern the lodge. According to regulations, the Secretary would be promoted to the position of Grand Master and President. But the old Grand Master could at least cling to the hope that he might evade his ultimate fate.

The Secretary addressed the members:

"My dear brothers, to our regret, it is our esteemed Grand Master who has been chosen by this draw. He has been leading our lodge conscientiously for many years and has gained our respect and, as you know, he has the right to request two additional draws. His argument that Frabato has used his magical powers to transmit the death sentence to him is quite understandable. I suggest that certain precautions be taken for the second draw, for we have forces at our disposal which are able to eliminate any interferences from Frabato. It is stated in our regulations that each member may turn the drum three times before the next draw. Let all in favor raise their hands."

All raised their right hands — even the Grand Master, marked for death. And yet the second draw weighed heavily on the souls of the brethren, for if the Grand Master were correct, then any one of them could be condemned this time around.

"The proposal has been unanimously accepted," the Secretary continued. "I thank you for the understanding you have shown towards our Grand Master. Our next step is to determine whether Frabato is exercising any influence on our lodge at this moment. We will confirm this with the help of our medium. Brother H., please go once more for the care-taker's daughter."

Brother H. left the hall and returned with the girl a short time later. The Secretary, who was not only a trained black magician but a skillful diplomat, welcomed her, saying:

"Dear Elli, I must apologize for disturbing you at this late hour, but we urgently need your assistance again. Some problems have arisen which we want to settle with your help. We shall compensate your trouble with a double fee."

Although she was well acquainted with the surroundings, it seemed to her that a particularly sinister mood lay over the hall. In spite of this, she answered in her natural way:

"I do not mind the late hour. For that much money I will be very pleased to help you."

A sofa had been placed in the middle of the hall, and Elli, accustomed to the procedure, willingly lay down upon it. Twenty-one of the brethren formed a circle around her, and the Secretary placed her into a deep hypnotic sleep. Then he evoked within her a state of clairvoyance and gave her the following order:

"Make a visit to Frabato in the spirit, and tell me what he is doing."

After a short hesitation, Elli briefly reported that Frabato was onstage, carrying out his usual demonstrations. When asked whether he were exercising any influence over her, she decisively said no.

The excitement in the hall increased considerably, for everyone began to feel that the Grand Master's previous assertions had been contradicted. The Secretary requested silence. The Grand Master sat in his chair looking pale, knowing full well that this wave of unrest was directed towards him. Suddenly he jumped up and cried into the hall:

"Frabato is influencing you all! And if he is not doing it himself, then he is sending his beings. He has thousands of them at his disposal!"

The charge that Frabato had thousands of spirit beings — whereas each member of the F.O.G.C. Lodge had only a single servant spirit — not only surprised those present, but greatly increased the anxiety in the hall.

The Grand Master realized his mistake immediately — instead of humiliating Frabato, he had humiliated himself and his own lodge.

Exhausted, he rested his head in his hands, murmuring in despair, "I am at the breaking point! I cannot go on any longer."

The Secretary loudly and energetically demanded silence and succeeded in calming the assembly. The twenty-one brethren still formed a circle round the sleeping girl, whom the Secretary once again addressed with a penetrating voice:

"When you wake up you will be free from any influences. No power in the world will be able to influence you, neither consciously nor unconsciously. No outside entity will be able to influence you. You will do everything of your own will."

Silently, he called four dark princes of the elements into the corners of the hall to assist in giving further protection against any magical influence. Visible only to the spiritual eye, these negative elemental princes guarded the progress of the ceremony. The formulas for their invocation were known only to the Grand Master and the Secretary.

After having completed the invocation, the Secretary assured the brethren of complete protection against any outside interference, and affirmed that only the highest divine providence would be able to exercise any influence.

The Grand Master's number was put into a new envelope and placed in the drum. The brothers who had formed the ring mentally repeated the necessary formula which rendered the magic circle effective.

The Secretary awakened the medium with the appropriate words; she stared with astonished into the bewildered faces surrounding her. Regaining her faculties, Elli thought that something unusual must have taken place during her sleep.

The Secretary carefully blindfolded her and led her to the drum, asking her to draw forth another envelope. Elli calmly reached inside and pulled one out.

A deathly silence reigned as everyone stared at the envelope. The Secretary took it and laid it on the table. Then he removed Elli's blindfold and quickly led her out of the hall. He asked her to wait for a quarter of an hour in an adjacent room, telling her that her help might be needed again.

Returning to the hall directly, he opened the fateful envelope with trembling hands and pulled out the number.

Again it was the number one.

A tortured moan escaped the Grand Master's chest; now, he felt, he was irretrievably lost. The other brethren heaved a sigh of relief; all their doubts disappeared, for the death sentence had found its mark. Nevertheless, the events of the evening caused a stir of conscience among some of them.

Full of expectation, the assembly directed its attention towards the Grand Master, who must now accept his sentence. At last he collected himself, but only enough to shout in mortal fear:

"Impossible! Impossible! I do not believe in this judgment. Something is going on here against me personally, to destroy me! Even if Frabato has not done this himself, there are forces at his disposal which are responsible for the whole thing. I claim my right to a third draw. Only then will I admit my defeat!"

A third draw had to be ratified by a majority vote. The Secretary rose to speak.

"It is the right of the condemned to demand a third draw. The third draw may be prevented if the required simple majority of votes is not present. Remember, to reject the Grand Master's right to such a draw will cast serious doubt on the validity of the process and even upon the statutes of the lodge. All those who approve of a third draw, please raise your hands."

The dramatic events of the evening had deeply disturbed the souls of many; they were torn between the fear of losing their own lives and the hope that the verdict would be confirmed yet a third time. After a few minutes, however, sixty members voted "yes" to a new draw. Fate could take its course.

During the preparations for the third draw, the Grand Master jumped to his feet and cried out wildly:

"This time I will draw the lot myself, for neither Frabato nor any other force in the world can influence me!"

After these words were spoken, the Secretary hurried out to pay Elli and send her home, informing her that her services were no longer required. Returning to the hall, he went straight to the drum and prepared it for the last time.

This time the procedure moved somewhat more rapidly, for the members gave their three turns to the drum hurriedly, anxious to be finished.

After the turning of the drum, the Secretary blindfolded

the Grand Master with the same cloth which had earlier been used for the medium. Again, breathless silence filled the hall. The Grand Master rummaged frantically among the envelopes. He seized one and pulled it forth. Before the Secretary was able to help him, he had torn the black bandage from his eyes and thrown it to the floor. With trembling hands, he opened the envelope and pulled out the number.

It was the number one.

He stared at it as if hypnotized; again the distorted demon face rose in front of him and scornful laughter filled his ears. He sank to the floor, unconscious.

They took the Grand Master into an adjacent room without further ado and made him rest on a sofa. His position as Grand Master and President of the lodge was irrevocably lost; now he was nothing but a candidate for death. In one of the next meetings, the Secretary would officially be appointed Grand Master of the lodge and the most astute among the other brethren would become the new Secretary.

The dramatic and tragic events of the past few hours left a deep impression on them all, one which they would remember as long as they lived. Although some had been in the lodge for many years, nothing like this evening's experience had ever occurred before.

The new Grand Master called a half-hour intermission. The hall emptied. There were many who needed some fresh air, and small groups gathered in the park to discuss the evening's events. Others tried to compose themselves in the lounge.

In ancient times, people were sacrificed to the gods. The same practice is alive and well in the F.O.G.C. Lodge, though their rituals have been brought into line with the present day. The laws of the lodge assert that one member must be sacrificed to the presiding demon each year. The drawing of the fatal lot has no bearing on whether a member has just joined the lodge or whether he has been there for many years.

The gong sounded, calling the brethren back to the hall. After everyone was seated, the new president rose and addressed the assembly, saying:

"My dear brethren, tonight we have completed the ceremony for choosing the victim who will be sacrificed to the lord of our lodge. This time it is a person whom we have all respected. Our lodge suffers a great loss with the Grand Master's departure. In spite of this, I believe that we can all go home this evening with the conviction that fraud is impossible when it comes to drawing lots for our annual sacrifice. Even though the activities of our lodge may rest on deception and lies, there is no cheating possible with this!

"Tonight's draw has shown that the laws of the lodge are supervised by the high forces of pitiless fate. Who would not have tried to save his own life, even as the Grand Master has done? The merits of our former Grand Master shall not be diminished by his behavior, and his name will remain with those of the most honorable members in the history of our lodge.

"In accordance with the lodge's statutes, any member leaving the lodge must be replaced by a new member. The replacement for Brother Silesius will be inducted tonight, and we shall fill my former position as Secretary at our next meeting. Brother F. has recommended one of his friends and has assured us that he vouches for the candidate's loyalty and discretion with his own life. Brother F., please bring in your friend."

A member of the circle left the hall and returned a few minutes later with a young man. The new Grand Master shook hands with him and welcomed him on behalf of the lodge. He apologized for the long wait by saying that unforeseen complications had arisen regarding certain rituals. The stranger had already agreed to the conditions for admission, therefore it was merely a matter of swearing him in and giving him a name and a number. The new member was given the number 2 and the lodge name "C."

With serious oaths, C. swore to abide by the lodge's statutes, and a demonic entity was assigned to him for the realization of his wishes. He was instructed in the ways and means of dealing with this being, and how he was to keep a journal of his activities. A formula was disclosed to him which could be used in combat telepathy and black magic. He was also informed of the lodge names of the other brethren, though not of their civil names. Only lodge names were used within the lodge.

When the initiation ceremony for the new member had ended, the new Grand Master officially closed the session. It was already past midnight; therefore the circle dissolved quickly, leaving only the new Grand Master behind to complete the lodge report. Upon finishing his work, he went to the room where the former president and Grand Master had been taken after his sentencing. Surprisingly enough, he was still lying on the sofa, half unconscious and unable to leave without assistance.

Since the new Grand Master was a member of the medical profession, he solved the problem in his own way. He quickly went for his bag of medical equipment and gave the condemned man a strong injection to stimulate the circulation of the blood. This got him to his feet within a few minutes. The Grand Master accompanied the despondent victim to his car. The driver was startled at the arrival of the two men, for he had fallen asleep during the long wait. He hastily opened the door for his master, the two lodge members quickly said goodbye to each other, and the former Grand Master let himself fall heavily back into the cushions. Then the door was closed and the car drove off into the night.

Pensively, the new Grand Master followed the car with his eyes. At last he turned back to the lodge buildings, carefully closed and locked all the doors and went home.

After an hour's journey, the deposed Grand Master of the F.O.G.C. Lodge arrived at his villa. The driver helped his employer into the house, taking his arm because he appeared sick and apathetic. The driver asked if there were any further orders, but was answered with a dismissive wave of the hand. The servant then disappeared quickly and silently.

Weakly, the Grand Master stumbled to his study and wearily stretched out on the sofa. Unable even to think of sleep, he stared constantly at the ceiling with expressionless eyes. Like a film, the most important events of his life passed through his mind: pictures of defamation, fraud, lies and murder. Remorse had been foreign to him for a long time. Even his uncertain future as a servant of the demons was not enough to bend his thoughts in a positive direction. Instead, rage and hatred for every kind of positive force held him captive, giving him a satisfaction possible only to a black magician.

The curses with which he had burdened himself, solely to acquire earthly goods! Now he had to leave everything behind, for he knew the spiritual laws, and that there was no salvation in this situation: there was no chance of escaping the demons.

Absent-mindedly he got up, poured some wine into a glass, and took a small packet of powder from a cabinet. He poured a little powder into the wine and lifted the glass to his lips with trembling hands, trying to shut out the scornful laughter which seemed to fill the entire room. Dizziness took hold of him, and with one swallow he emptied the glass. A burning sensation made him leap up for a moment, and he stood there spellbound, gazing into the distance. Then the glass slipped from his hand and shattered. He staggered and sank lifeless to the floor as the poison did its work.

Thus ended the life of the black magician S., executed by his own hand.

Chapter VII

It had been another exciting evening. The audience had witnessed mysterious and magical demonstrations, and afterwards Frabato had spent more than two hours answering questions from reporters and other interested persons. Now he was glad that the excitement was over and that he was finally able to return to his hotel. It was already midnight by the time he entered his room. Soon he was lying in bed, tired and worn out, trying to catch a longed-for rest.

Oddly enough, despite his fatigue he could not fall asleep. He changed position several times without success. He had just made another attempt to relax himself by deliberately silencing his thoughts when he suddenly felt a strange force in the room. A gray cloud intensified in the middle of the floor, becoming brighter and brighter at the center and emitting countless sparks of light. These scintilla of light set circles moving round the room in all the colors of the rainbow, interwoven like the colors in a kaleidoscope.

A rustling was heard as the light in the cloud condensed more and more. Frabato, initiated in every possible magical practice, at once focused his clairvoyant vision upon the apparition and recognized that a highly evolved being from the zone girdling the earth, one already well known to him, was announcing his visit.

Frabato surmised that the visit must be an important one; why else would such an entity appear, uncalled for, at this time of night? The entity was condensing on its own power, whereas normally such a materialization only took place through a great expenditure of energy on the part of the person concerned.

Before Frabato's eyes, the cloud of light formed into the shape of a spiritual being. The entity directed his brilliant gaze towards Frabato, addressing him with serious intent:

"Frabato, you are in danger! You must leave this country before noon tomorrow. Through lies and defamation your enemies have managed to have you accused of treason. This political suspicion is a threat to your life; therefore act quickly! A warrant for your arrest has already been issued. Escape is your only option; an open conflict with the fanatic ideology which rules this land would be altogether senseless. Leave all your belongings behind. Hurry to escape! I warn you!"

The last words were spoken as if from afar. The being dissolved into a light mist which, in turn, slowly dissipated. The room became dark again, and only a pleasant fragrance lingering in the quiet reminded him of the strange visit.

Frabato was fully awake now. He knew this particular intelligence well and had no doubt that its words of warning were based upon something quite real. Before planning his escape, he remembered to surround himself completely with the Akasha, so that his thoughts and plans would remain invisible to the spiritual world. Otherwise his enemies might have been able to learn of his plans with the help of certain entities or a trance medium. The secret of complete isolation and the ability to obliterate anything imprinted in the Akasha was an art unknown to his enemies. Only a few people on earth, who, like Frabato, belonged to the Brothers of Light, knew these secrets and their practical application.

Frabato worked out a plan of escape. He found it difficult to leave behind everything he had established here, but the situation demanded that all his earthly possessions and advantages be abandoned in order that he might simply escape with his life. He knew he had to take precautions, for he knew his enemies' methods. He had to be more skillful than they, and he had to act before it was too late.

It was nearly dawn when he finally finished his plan. In order to rest until it was time to go, he performed a set of special meditations which would help make up for his lost sleep.

Frabato rose at seven o'clock and washed with cold water in order to appear refreshed and rested. As he was dressing, he looked as if he had slept well all night. He carefully distributed his money and documents in his suit pockets. Shortly afterwards, he was on his way to the hotel restaurant for breakfast.

He sat down at an empty table and placed his order. He had planned to visit the hotel manager in his office but was spared the effort, for the manager, as if directed by a good fate, entered the breakfast room. Frabato beckoned to him and invited him to sit at his table. The manager, who was a friendly and obliging gentleman, gladly shook his hand and welcomed him:

"Good morning, sir. Have you slept well? Is there anything I can do for you? I hope you have a pleasant stay."

Frabato remained quiet while the manager sat down opposite him, then said, "I am very pleased with your hospitality, food, and staff. You can be sure that I will recommend your hotel wherever the occasion may arise. As you know, I intend to stay with you for another fortnight and I would kindly ask you to take some money in advance so that I am not too much indebted to you."

He reached into his breast pocket and gave the manager the money. The manager made a gesture to indicate that there was no need for pre-payment, but Frabato persuaded him to accept it anyway. Shortly afterwards, the manager brought him a receipt from the office.

He was used to peculiar habits on the part of his guests; therefore he suspected nothing. Nor was he displeased with the arrangement, for of course some guests left without paying anything at all. Apart from that, he was honored by the continued presence of Frabato, who, in a very short time, had become quite a celebrity.

Taking the receipt, Frabato said, "You know I am always beset by reporters and other interested people. I have an appointment with a friend of mine, and I am going to the café near the city tower. I will be back in about two hours. Should anyone want to see me in the meantime, please tell him I will be returning."

The manager had no reason to be suspicious, and assured Frabato that he could be relied upon. Frabato took his leave and, shortly afterwards, disappeared into the big-city traffic.

Dressed in only a suit, without a coat or hat, Frabato strolled down the narrow street before finally walking towards a familiar taxi stand. There were a few taxis waiting there; the drivers, engaged in animated conversation, were smoking. Frabato called out his destination, one of the drivers offered his services, and off they went. After about three kilometers they reached their destination. Frabato paid the fare and mingled with the pedestrians again.

Frabato knew of another taxi stand nearby, and made his way there. There was only one taxi available, and Frabato ordered the driver to take him to the train station, where he disappeared. From there he spent a few moments carefully observing the taxis parked outside, though without noticing anyone suspicious. He then chose a private taxi, a big car with a six-cylinder engine. Sitting down in the back, he pulled a hundred-mark note from his pocket and gave it to the driver, saying:

"I have to get to the border quickly. I have just received a telegram that my father is dying, and I need to get home as soon as possible. I will pay you double for every kilometer you can go faster than the speed limit."

His passenger's stern face, together with the hundred-mark banknote, convinced the driver at once. In no time they were racing towards the border. The driver never suspected that this was an escape.

While Frabato was hurrying towards the border, two gentlemen entered his hotel in Dresden and inquired for him at the reception desk. They were informed that Frabato would be back at about 10:30 A.M.

The two gentlemen did not take seats in the restaurant; instead, they walked up and down in front of the hotel until the moment had passed when Frabato was expected to return.

Then the two visitors began to get impatient. They went to see the manager and pulled out their identity cards, saying, "Criminal Police Department! Can you tell us the whereabouts of Frabato?"

The manager, who had been unpleasantly surprised at first, felt relieved when he heard that they were only looking for their good friend Frabato.

"Gentlemen," he replied, "Frabato has no idea that you are looking for him. This morning he gave me a fortnight's advance payment for his room. His car is in the garage, his suits and his other clothes are in his room. He said he was meeting a friend at the café near the city tower. Surely he is merely late and will be here in a moment."

The two gentlemen thanked the manager and left their telephone number with him, asking him to call them the moment Frabato returned. Then they left the hotel quickly.

The two police officers hurried to the café and asked the staff if Frabato had been there. When they heard that no one had seen him, they informed their office that they suspected Frabato had fled. In no time at all, a large number of policemen were on their way to the various taxi stands to try and ascertain Frabato's whereabouts. With the help of photographs and personal descriptions they soon found a trace of the magician — but this trace failed to lead them to the man they were looking for. The police were forced to reluctantly admit that their suspect had eluded them.

Meanwhile, after a wild ride, Frabato reached the border at 11:30 A.M. He thanked the driver, paid him double the fare, and walked casually up to the border station. Not having any luggage, he was able to pass through without delay.

The taxi driver wanted his engine to cool down a bit, so he leaned contentedly in his seat and lit a cigarette. "I should have passengers like that every day," he thought.

Frabato had just passed customs and entered his native country when a voice came over the loudspeakers on the German side:

"Attention! Attention! All border stations of the German Reich! The stage artist Frabato is trying to escape the German authorities and is to be arrested at once. It is presumed that he is using a taxi to escape over the border."

A detailed description of Frabato followed. With a sigh of relief, Frabato walked towards the border town, thinking, "It was a close call, but I made it!" He was safe now in his native country. He had thwarted another plan designed by the F.O.G.C. Lodge. His possessions, however, had been abandoned, and he would have to adapt to a new lifestyle. He did not have much money, but he hoped he could manage for a while.

While having lunch in the station restaurant of the small town, he thought about what had happened in the past few hours and how he had barely escaped with his life. He thanked Divine Providence for his rescue. An hour later he was on an express train bound for the capital of his native land.

Chapter VIII

Frabato awoke in his hotel room, deeply concerned about the direction of history. Mankind's chronic inability to envision positive thoughts and transform them into deeds was becoming even more widespread. Political persecution, coupled with torture and murder, had become the order of the day — and would soon lead to an orgy of destruction. With his spiritual eyes, Frabato could see the course of events to come in the Akasha, but the immutable laws of silence did not permit him to discuss such matters in public. His own fate, too, would take a tragic turn, and he would not be allowed to use his magical powers to alter his destiny, for every being in the universe is bound by the laws of karma.

He felt some consolation, though, in the fact that Divine Providence would sustain him during his time of persecution. He knew he was protected by the Brothers of Light in order that he might carry out his mission on earth.

To rid himself of these depressing thoughts he took refuge for some minutes in a special meditation. Then he had a bath and shortly afterwards left the hotel quite refreshed.

The inhabitants of the metropolis seemed to have made "haste" and "speed" their slogans, for there was already a nervous hustle and bustle in many streets of the city. Frabato chose a restaurant on a quiet side street for his breakfast. At the next table, three gentlemen were engaged in lively conversation. Contrary to his usual habit, Frabato took up a newspaper to familiarize himself with his new surroundings. He was in no hurry; as of yet, he had no plans for the future.

While reading his paper, he overheard some of the conversation at the next table, especially because one of the three gentlemen was explaining his views rather loudly and enthusi-astically. Frabato's interest was suddenly aroused as he realized that metaphysics and spiritism constituted the subject matter of the conversation. He proceeded to watch the three men inconspicuously, though without making use of his clair-voyance, and he deduced that one of the gentlemen was a scientist, whereas the other two appeared to be businessmen. After listening to their opinions for a few moments, he was unable to suppress a smile at the way so many confused and quite incorrect ideas had been mixed together.

One of the men happened to look in Frabato's direction and notice his indulgent smile. For a moment the man was unable to make up his mind between two possibilities: either this smiling gentleman at the next table knew more about the subject of conversation than the speakers themselves, or he thought their entire topic a mere chimera.

Finally he decided that the former was the case, despite the fact that Frabato's appearance did not allow for any definite conclusions; he looked like an average person, a man in the street.

During a short pause in the conversation, the man who had been watching Frabato whispered something to his friends. The other two looked at Frabato and then nodded. The first gentleman got up at once and approached Frabato's table:

"Pardon my disturbing you, sir, but it would appear that you are an expert in occultism. May I therefore invite you to join in our conversation. My name is K., and I am a manu-facturer of optical instruments."

Frabato accepted the invitation in a friendly manner. Having introduced himself, he sat down at the neighboring table. Mr. K. introduced his partners: Mr. P., a bank manager, and Professor G., a doctor of chemistry. The professor was unable to control his curiosity:

"Mr. Frabato, are you not the clairvoyant and occultist

about whom so many newspapers have been reporting for some time now? If that is indeed the case, then I must regard it as my good fortune to meet you here."

Frabato, who now realized that he could not remain unnoticed in this city, nodded to the professor, saying:

"Yes, I am the one you have read about in the papers. You really are lucky to meet me here, for, strictly speaking, my presence here is rather involuntary. I did not intend to laugh at you, but some of your views on metaphysics are not exactly correct."

Of course, the gentlemen wanted to know why Frabato had come to the city involuntarily. He told them the whole story and, shocked, they promised to help him as much as they could. They all invited him to their homes, and, since he had no fixed plans, he decided to dedicate the following three nights to his new acquaintances. One of the evenings would involve a small celebration with a few friends and acquaintances — Frabato took it as an act of fate and benevolently agreed. (As a matter of fact, he later found so much support in this circle that he was able to overcome his desperate situation.)

First, the gentlemen asked him many questions about occult phenomena, which Frabato answered as clearly as possible. However, he pointed out that there was a great deal of knowledge in the field which could only reveal itself to a real practitioner. The three men soon admitted that they had been seeing many things in the wrong light. After two hours had passed, they began to discuss the problem of fate. The professor was of the opinion that there was no such thing as pre-determined fate, but that man was the architect of his own destiny. Although the professor gave good reasons for his views, Frabato responded with amused laughter.

"Professor," he said, "a person must travel quite a ways along the spiritual path and attain a certain maturity in his development before he can become the master of his own fate; moreover, he must be able to sustain that maturity under all possible circumstances. To say it in a few words, one must attain spiritual, astral, and physical equilibrium if one wishes to take the reins of his destiny into his own hands. If you think you have reached such a level of maturity and can determine your fate yourself, I shall give you a small demonstration of the influence of destiny upon man."

There was a pause; the three gentlemen stared at Frabato, astounded. One could see from the professor's countenance that he was very perturbed, for he had always set the tone in this small group and now felt somewhat demoted. Frabato noticed this and said, benevolently:

"I do not wish to deny that you have a great deal of *theoretical* knowledge. You have read much, even in foreign languages. You have a large library, and you have been publishing articles on metaphysics in different foreign magazines, which has given you a name as something of an authority. But in occult science there is a great difference between mere knowledge and practical know-how."

The professor was quite surprised at what Frabato knew about him. Curious, he replied, "Mr. Frabato, if what you say is true I should be very pleased to see you produce any evidence of the influence of destiny."

Lost in thought, Frabato gazed ahead. His faraway eyes had assumed a peculiar stare. His consciousness was clearly not focused upon his immediate surroundings.

This condition lasted only a short time, then Frabato blinked his eyes as if awakening from a deep sleep, smiled at the professor, and said:

"I have just been looking into your future with my spiritual eye. With the help of a small event, I shall prove to you the influence of fate. If you are not anywhere near the Pulver Tower at midnight tonight, you will have proven that you are able to master your fate. Let us wait and see if it is within your power to resist your destiny."

94

The professor's countenance exuded irony and arrogance as he retorted, "I will wager anything that I will not be at the Pulver Tower at midnight!"

Frabato pretended not to hear these words, and changed the subject by confirming the dates of his invitations. Everyone had another glass of wine, then they all took their leave.

When he left the restaurant and climbed into a taxi, Professor G. felt rather peculiar. For a bachelor, he lived in high style, for he resided in a big villa and had a number of servants. His versatile research work was one reason for his being alone; the other was that he took no particular interest in women. Still, he engaged in love affairs from time to time, but wanted to remain free of the obligations attached to family life.

Arriving home, he found a lot of mail. He merely skimmed through it. He scribbled some notes on some of the letters but postponed his replies to a later date. He was not able to free himself from the bad mood which had beset him at the restaurant shortly before the end of the conversation. He would never have admitted, though, that his offended self-conceit was the cause of his mood. What sort of man was this Frabato?, he wondered. During their initial meeting, the magician had been able to describe many details of the professor's home. It was as if he had already been there.

"This Frabato will prove to be incorrect tonight," he said to himself. "I will show him that I am the master of my destiny! I shall make a great effort not to leave my home again this evening."

He decided to stay in bed the whole time, no matter what happened. What a satisfaction it would be for him to prove that Frabato was wrong! His own self-esteem would grow and, apart from that, he would verify the validity and incontestability of his philosophical opinions.

A glance at his watch made him realize that it was

already 3:00 P.M. That was why his stomach had been grumbling so energetically; he had not yet had lunch. After he had eaten something, he tried to work on a report he was to send to a foreign magazine, but had quite a difficult time concentrating because Frabato's words kept nagging at his soul like a worm and he was afraid that the magician might turn out to be right in the end.

At 5:00 P.M. G.'s thoughts were still occupied with Frabato. To rid himself of his mental aggravation, he went to bed and decided not to get up before the next morning. But his inward unrest would not let him sleep. Nervously, he tossed and turned.

Suddenly, a servant knocked at his door to inform him that a party of well-known artists had come to visit him and that they were now waiting in the foyer. Professor G. had good connections with the art world, for apart from his academic activities he was also a theater critic.

The visitors seemed to have had a few glasses of wine somewhere and were all slightly inebriated. When the servant returned to inform them that the professor was not feeling well and therefore had gone to bed early, they could not be kept back, but literally stormed his room.

"What is the matter with you, old boy, creeping into bed at this time of the day? You are not ill. You need a little change!" one of the visitors exclaimed — a man well known for his witty humor who was never short of words. The artists badgered the professor insistently in an attempt to persuade him to get out of bed. Since there was no sign of illness, the professor was in a weak position and eventually had to get dressed. In the meantime his visitors made themselves comfortable in the living room and the professor had no choice but to offer a few bottles of wine because of his long-standing friendship with them. The comedian, who was also a leading actor on major stages, gave a most vivid account of the latest news, and soon the professor forgot all about

Frabato's prophecy. The actor finished his stories by leaning towards the professor and saying, "My dear friend, you absolutely must come to the theater with us this evening! Tonight is the première of a play in which I happen to have the main role. As a critic, you must not miss it under any circumstances."

After two glasses of wine, the professor was mildly intoxicated and accepted the invitation by nodding his head. He quickly had something prepared for supper, which pleased the cheerful company very much. Then the time came when they set out. Two big taxis were called to take the happy lot to the theater, where the professor had his own box.

The opening night was a grand success and the professor waited with his friends in the foyer for the leading actor to appear. When the star finally arrived, everyone gave him their hearty congratulations and the professor promised to write a very favorable critique. A few more actors joined them and the whole troupe went to a wine tavern to celebrate the play's success.

As the actors had another performance the next day, the company gradually dissolved around 11:30. The leading actor said good-bye to the professor at the door.

"Good night! Why not take a taxi? You will get home quickly."

But it was a Saturday night and the clubs were rather busy; there was not a taxi in sight. Because he had been drinking, the professor decided to get some fresh air by walking part of the way home.

The traffic on the main street was still heavy, so he turned down a side street which seemed less frequented; he had had enough excitement for one day. Music filled his ears from the half-open windows of the pubs and night clubs as he strolled along, completely absorbed in thought.

Suddenly there was a commotion near one of the taverns. A number of men and women were standing together in a group. Curious, the professor approached them and realized that two young men, obviously drunk, had insulted each other and were beginning to fight.

Unfortunately, G. felt compelled to call out to the two men, telling them to go home and not fight in the streets.

Everything changed at once. The two drunks stopped fighting. One of them began to insult the professor, who in turn reacted with harsh words. One of the ruffians moved in on him, threateningly. G. gave the other a slap, just as his attacker grabbed him. With that, a commotion ensued; everyone shouted, and then the second ruffian turned towards him.

Professor G. could see that he did not have a chance. He hastily pushed himself through the crowd and ran away. The man he had hit was eager for revenge and, taking a knife out of his pocket, ran after the professor, cursing at the top of his voice.

Gasping for air, G. turned into a busier street, hoping to find a policeman there. "My God, where are they when you need them?" He was running for his life, but his assailant was gradually gaining on him. By now he was almost exhausted. As he turned the corner at the Pulver Tower, Frabato suddenly stood in his way.

"Help me!" the professor cried out, panting heavily, his eyes filled with fear. "They want to murder me!"

Frabato gently pushed the professor aside. "Stop running and do not be afraid!" he said, kindly. Then he calmly stepped in front of the approaching ruffian, who suddenly seemed paralyzed, the knife still in his hand. Then he turned, cursing, and disappeared around the next corner. Frabato had changed the situation to the professor's advantage with the use of a Kabbalistic word.

Frabato then turned to the professor, whose head by now had cleared but whose limbs were still filled with fear. He was stuttering slightly as he said to Frabato, "If you had not turned up, I would be a corpse by now!"

Frabato patted his shoulder and, pointing to his watch, said:

"My dear professor, you still do not seem to be quite the master of your fate, for otherwise you would not be here at this hour. Things have turned out as I predicted. I hope you are now convinced that one cannot be master of his fate if he is still unable to control all his circumstances and lead them in the direction he chooses. And you will now realize that one must achieve what is called 'magical equilibrium' in order to accomplish this."

G. realized he had been beaten. He apologized for having been a fool, naming his self-conceit as the culprit. Frabato led him to a busier street and invited him for a cup of coffee to calm his nerves. They stepped into a restaurant. A gypsy band was entertaining the guests, but Frabato took the professor to a quiet table in a corner. Frabato's self-assurance quieted G., and he soon regained his customary self-confidence. Now he wanted details, and while they were having their coffee Frabato told him he had foreseen this event in the Akasha. It would have been possible for Frabato to turn up at the moment of the fight, but that would have been somewhat less convincing.

"How long did you wait at the Pulver Tower?" G. asked.

"Only about five minutes," Frabato replied, "for I was able to follow you with my spiritual eye and I therefore knew where to meet you."

Professor G. was full of admiration over these fateful connections. He asked Frabato many questions that night, questions which Frabato answered in great detail.

At last the two night owls ventured forth and, promising to meet again at K.'s the following night, they took a cab home.

*

Evening had fallen. Preparations for the great party had been completed at K.'s villa. A number of K.'s friends and acquaintances, all interested in occult science, had gathered early. Frabato was known to many of the guests from newspaper reports, and they were therefore eager to meet him personally.

K. had already telephoned G. in the morning to find out about the events of the previous night. The professor had spoken only briefly, but promised to give a detailed account of the story that evening.

One car after another arrived, bringing guests. The host was always very pleased to be the center of big social events. A mixed company of industrialists, writers, artists, and reporters was gathering. At half past seven, K. welcomed his guests with a few words, announcing that Frabato would arrive at eight o'clock. He asked his friend G. for an account of his experiences. The professor told his story impressively and exhaustively, along with Frabato's prophecy.

His accounts of the previous evening enhanced everyone's expectations of Frabato, for many of the guests wanted to ask him for advice concerning personal matters. When his arrival was finally announced to the master of the house, there was an immediate hush.

K. led Frabato in, introduced him with a few words, and had supper served at once in order to create a casual atmosphere. The host had spared no expense: the guests were offered a large selection of the best foods and the most exquisite drinks. Frabato had taken the seat of honor at the head of the table and made use of this opportunity to study each of the guests inconspicuously. By the time the table was cleared, he already had an idea of their most secret thoughts, though he gave the impression that he was not interested in any one particular person.

Then, as the most interesting part of the evening was to begin, K. worried that his guests might impose upon Frabato.

Frabato came to his rescue and rose to thank his host for the invitation, praising his excellent hospitality and expressing how pleased he was that so many friends of the house were very interested in the occult sciences.

K., clearly pleased with these words, began telling everyone how he had chanced to meet Frabato. About half an hour of general conversation went by, and some of the guests began to get anxious that they would be unable to exchange a word with Frabato that evening. On top of that, many of them had been expecting occult phenomena.

Frabato asked for a cup of coffee and, while stirring in some sugar, started to speak:

"Ladies and gentlemen! Most of you have already heard of magic mirrors and crystal balls. A true initiate, though, is also able to use any liquid as a magic mirror — even a cup of black coffee."

An actress was about to ask a question when Frabato motioned her to silence with his hand.

"I know you are about to ask whether your performance tomorrow will be a success, since you are playing a new role and you have made some mistakes at the dress rehearsal."

He looked into his cup of coffee with intense concentration, as if reading the event directly from it, although in fact the black surface simply enabled him to look into the future with his spiritual eye.

"You may rest assured," he went on. "It will be a big success and there will be great applause for you."

The actress was pleasantly surprised and, knowing that Frabato was able to read her most secret thoughts, she felt unable to say a word. In any case, she was very pleased with what she heard.

"None of you need say a word to me," Frabato continued. "I shall tell everyone what burdens him most."

He then addressed one of the businessmen in a serious tone: "Your future looks bleak, for the agreement you signed two days ago will soon bankrupt you."

The gentleman in question had in fact signed such an agreement, and was now deeply shocked to hear such a prophecy. Unfortunately, what Frabato had declared was soon to come true.

In the same manner, Frabato revealed the near future to all the guests. When everyone had had his turn and a young lady was about to ask another question, Frabato put his right forefinger to his mouth to indicate silence. Immediately, everyone became quiet, watching Frabato with curiosity. The magician was staring into a corner of the room as if he perceived something extraordinary there. For a few seconds his countenance took on an absent-minded expression, then he inhaled deeply and, turning towards K., said:

"My dear friend, it was not right for you to leave your youngest sister alone upstairs in her room. You have been telling her about me today, and she was very much looking forward to being able to speak to me too. You need not have been ashamed to place your afflicted sister among us, for illness is no shame. I can see her crying bitterly."

Frabato's words both surprised K. and embarrassed him deeply. He managed a faint-hearted admission that he had not intended to have his suffering sister mix with the guests lest the atmosphere be spoiled. This, he said, had been the only reason for his decision, and he was now quite shaken that it had not remained hidden from Frabato. If none of those present had any objection, he would now go and bring down his sister.

K.'s suggestion was unanimously approved, and two ladies volunteered to help the disabled girl to dress.

K. went up to his sister with the two ladies; she was indeed lying on her bed with her eyes full of tears.

Helen, K.'s sister, had suffered a cerebral hemorrhage six

months earlier and had been paralyzed on her right side ever since. The best doctors had tried to treat her, but there was still no hope of a cure. She was only twenty-three years old.

K. told his sister what had happened and asked her to spend the rest of the evening with Frabato and the other guests. Because of her helplessness, Helen refused to join them at first. But when the ladies offered their help, curiosity and anticipation got the better of her and she agreed to join in. K. left the room, the ladies began to dress Helen, and she was carried downstairs on a chair. Everyone present welcomed her cordially and she beamed with pleasure when she was given the seat of honor beside Frabato.

To keep the party going, Frabato gave an account of some interesting events he had experienced on his numerous journeys. The guests listened attentively but secretly hoped for further evidence of Frabato's occult abilities and, consequently, were full of anticipation. Frabato did not fail to notice, for all their thoughts lay open to his spiritual eyes. Without letting it show outwardly, he was busying himself with Helen's destiny. In his mind, Frabato asked Divine Providence for permission to cure this woman and, as if from a profound depth, he received an answer from the unfathomable abyss: "You may help her, cure her!"

Frabato now interrupted his account. With everyone's eyes fixed steadily upon him, he seized Helen's hands and gazed at her for a few seconds. She fell into deep sleep at once. No one moved. After about two minutes, Helen began to breathe deeply, her eyelashes blinking softly. Then she was awake again.

Frabato was still holding her hands when he said to her quietly, "You are healthy again. How do you feel?"

The young woman looked around the circle doubtfully, then, hesitatingly, lifted her right arm and moved her fingers. She bent and stretched her right leg; she was happy behind all comprehension!

"You may now use both your legs again," Frabato said with a smile. When she got up, still rather unsteady in her movements, Frabato held her arm and accompanied her as she took her first steps. Then she went on alone, cautiously, fearing that she might still fall back into the old condition. Not until she had walked a few meters without anyone's help was she convinced that she had been completely healed. Tears of happiness sparkled in her eyes as everyone congratulated her on this unexpected cure.

While the guests were sharing Helen's happiness, Frabato quietly went to the bar. This way he could avoid any flattery — being made a saint was the last thing he wanted. Most of the guests simply stood in awe of the healing, while others felt rather eerie in the presence of someone who had real power over the health and sickness of human beings. Later, Helen joined Frabato at the bar and, stretching out her hand, she said, "I am very, very happy. You have given me my life back and I really do not know how to thank you!"

With a slight bow Frabato took her hand and replied, "It was a pleasure for me, but I was only the tool. Your thanks are due to no one else but Divine Providence, who has made this healing possible."

Released from the depressing burden of illness, Helen mingled with the guests again. The party's mood had reached its peak, and the evening's events were enthusiastically discussed in a number of small groups. It was after midnight when the guests finally said goodnight to their host.

After the last guest had left the house, only K., his sister Helen, and Frabato remained. K. invited Frabato to stay with them for the night — an invitation which he gratefully accepted, since he felt very tired. Only a few minutes went by before this little group dissolved as well, and Frabato retreated to the guest room for the night.

*

The rays of the rising sun found their way through the curtains and settled on Frabato's face; it did not take long before the sunlight woke him. He got up, dressed, and was about to leave his room when there was a cautious knock at his door. When he opened it, K. and his sister stood there beaming with joy, wishing him a good morning and inviting him to breakfast. Both had slept very little during the night due to the after-effect of the evening's excitement. Despite all this, Frabato's presence in the house persuaded them to rise early that morning as well.

They sat down for a comfortable breakfast which Helen had prepared for them. K. at once addressed Frabato:

"Master, we should like to make a suggestion. We have a country house in one of the suburbs which is presently unoccupied. You can live there for as long as you wish without cost. Apart from that, we should be very pleased if we could also count on your friendly advice in the future."

After a short consideration, Frabato replied, "I thank you very much for this proposal. I gladly accept it, for a hotel room is by no means a place of comfort. You may always count on my advice and help."

Breakfast ended and they went together to the hotel for Frabato's luggage and then drove to K.'s country house. The house was completely furnished and was situated in charming rural surroundings. After K. and his sister made sure that Frabato was supplied with the necessary household goods, they said goodbye to their guest.

Frabato was quite content with the course of his fate. A house was now at his disposal in which he was able to work undisturbed. He had become acquainted with some of the most influential people of the city, who would, no doubt, help him financially as well. On the whole, fate was showing him its sunny side.

* * *

Chapter IX

It was not long before Frabato was fully occupied in his new residence. He wrote commentaries on the science of metaphysics for various magazines. Reporters came to visit him more frequently, and he was more and more often asked for help by the ailing. As he was also well-versed in the art of healing, he was able to treat many cases successfully, as long as the laws of karma allowed him to do so.

Late in the afternoon of such a busy day, the last visitor had just left the house and Frabato was making a few preparations for the next day. The bell announced another guest. In the reception room, Frabato encountered professor G., who greeted him cordially. G. was a regular visitor and the two of them often discussed various aspects of occult science at great length.

Frabato shook hands with G., saying, "I have had many visitors today and I have not yet had a chance to relax. I should like to go for a walk in nature. The weather today is lovely and a bit of fresh air will not do us any harm. What do you think?"

G. agreed, and a few minutes later they left the house together and walked towards a nearby forest surrounded by fields and meadows. As the sun was already rather low, it had lost its scorching strength, but the heat was still rising from the soil and all nature seemed parched. As on his former visits, G. had prepared a number of questions on occult problems which Frabato would answer in detail. Today he had a few questions concerning elemental beings and the spirits of nature. Frabato gave the professor a precise account of the various kinds of elemental beings together with their methods of working, both in nature and in human beings. In so doing, he pointed out that the beings of nature are especially fond of the people who likewise feel close to nature.

They walked on in silence for a while, wrapped in thought and listening to the voices of nature. Although the sun was gradually disappearing behind the horizon, it was still quite hot and there was not a cloud to be seen in the clear sky.

"I know," Frabato began, "that you are a great skeptic. Being a theoretician, you find it difficult to form a clear picture of the powers of magic. As you can see for yourself, there is no hope of rain at the moment. Despite this, I will now use the Kabbalistic magic of nature in order to bring about some rainfall within a very short time. This is to convince you of the effectiveness of this science."

"That sounds unbelievable," G. retorted, "but no secret seems to be hidden from you. I would of course be very grateful to you for demonstrating such an example of natural magic."

Frabato smiled faintly, for he knew that control over natural magic is one of the perfectly normal abilities of a magician.

"You see," he said to G., "nothing is impossible for a human being who is united with Divine Providence. However, the true adept will always move within divine order, since he is fully responsible for everything he does. The more perfect an initiate's development, the greater will be his respect for Divine Providence and the magnificent secrets of the cosmos. I shall not make rain simply to convince you, but also to satisfy nature, which is craving for water. Please watch the sky carefully and remain quiet until I speak again."

The two wanderers sat down in the grass and were looking over the vast fields. There were no people nearby and they were completely unobserved and undisturbed.

Frabato assumed a yogic asana, crossing his legs and

keeping his back upright. His eyes closed; he seemed completely paralyzed. G. examined nature attentively, and from time to time cast a shy glance at the rigid Frabato. It might have been about five minutes before Frabato's figure came back to life. He opened his eyes, and, stretching his legs, sat beside G., asking him:

"Well, have you noticed anything extraordinary?"

Indeed, G. had already noticed a gradually increasing tension in the air — the promise of a thunderstorm! The wind was growing stronger and stronger. When Frabato started to speak to him, the first clouds appeared on the horizon, and G. now pointed into the distance, full of astonishment:

"Just look how quickly the clouds are approaching! It is indeed phenomenal that you should have such mighty powers at your disposal. From your appearance, no one would guess at your abilities."

"It is not necessary for a true magician to make a show of his knowledge and abilities. He can adapt himself inconspicuously to any circumstances and thus remain undetected by the average man. This adaptability is an aspect of silence and, from the Hermetic point of view, is one of the basic characteristics of divine power. Silence, in the magical sense, does not mean that one should refrain from talking; rather, one is to hide one's spiritual abilities from the public. Only when this principle is observed will Divine Providence trust a mature human being with the highest power. When we first met, you did not have the slightest suspicion that I was engaged in the Hermetic and spiritual sciences. Even if we were to know each other for many years, you would only be able to perceive as much of my abilities as is possible in accordance with your own level of development. In any case, a true adept will never run about with a halo."

During this short conversation the sky had become overcast and the atmosphere charged, as though a thunderstorm were about to break loose at any moment. In fact, lightning was flashing through the clouds and thunder was rumbling. Professor G. looked at the sky anxiously and seemed ill at ease being in the open country at that moment. To soothe him, Frabato put his hand on his shoulder, saying:

"As long as I am here with you, you need not be afraid. It is warm, indeed, and a few raindrops will not do us any harm. Apart from that, there is a bushy chestnut tree near here for our shelter. However, should you want to get home before the thunderstorm, I will join you."

G. seemed appeased and agreed to the suggestion that they take refuge from the rain under the chestnut tree. It was only about twenty meters away, and the first heavy raindrops began falling to the ground even before they got there. Within a few seconds the rain began in earnest, and, running the last few steps, they reached the tree. Strong gusts of wind were now blowing through the trees, mercilessly breaking the weaker branches. The rain poured down heavily, puddles and pools forming everywhere. The soil could not absorb the water quickly enough — it had been a long time since there had been a thunderstorm as strong as this one in that part of the country.

The winds whipped through the chestnut tree and soon it could not offer much shelter. Both men got thoroughly wet. This did not spoil Frabato's good mood, but G., being less resistant, began to shiver from the cold.

"Unfortunately, I am very sensitive," he said, trying to make an excuse. "I will certainly catch cold in these wet clothes."

"Do not be afraid," said Frabato, putting his right hand on the professor's shoulder.

After a few seconds G. looked at Frabato unbelievingly. "You are transferring heat into me from your hand! I am already as hot as if I were in a steam bath. Now I understand how you can also cure the sick with an extraordinary power like that."

He was silent for a moment, and then, after a deep breath, he went on: "If I only had a tiny part of your power, how happy I should be!"

The sky seemed to have opened and the soil could not absorb all the water: the ditches had already filled and the paths were flooded. Shyly, G. asked, "How long will this rain go on? We will not be able to go home in this thunderstorm."

Frabato looked at him with a smile and replied, "Just as I have caused the weather spirits to bring rain, I shall now ask them to stop it."

"That is impossible!" the professor exclaimed. "The whole sky is dark and we cannot even think of going home!"

Frabato laughed and said, "Why not? As soon as we leave this spot here, not a drop of rain will fall any longer. Or do you doubt that this will happen? I shall prove to you that with God everything is possible. Why should such a little thing not be possible? Now watch carefully!"

Frabato raised his hand in their intended direction. Then he whispered a few words and made a gesture in the air. Only a few seconds had passed before it did in fact stop raining, although the color of the sky had not changed in any way. Frabato beckoned G. to follow him. The professor quickly joined Frabato and although they were both completely soaked, Frabato seemed to be in high spirits.

These miracles were completely beyond the professor's powers of comprehension. Much to his surprise, he suddenly realized that where Frabato and he were walking it was not raining, while everywhere else it continued to pour. Looking up, he noticed that the clouds were parting directly above them and were closing again behind them. He had never before witnessed such a phenomenon.

Without saying a word, Frabato walked at the professor's side, noticing his surprise with pleasure. All the way back to the country house, not one drop fell on the two men as the thunderstorm and rain continued to rage everywhere else.

When they reached Frabato's residence, the sky was still dark and they had to switch on the lights. G. wanted to go home at once but Frabato persuaded him to stay and lent him some dry clothes, giving the wet ones to his servant to be dried and ironed.

They then sat down comfortably in the living room with a cup of tea and some biscuits.

"You are a peculiar man! You make it rain, you stop the rain, you cure any ailment, you are familiar with all the sciences of the world — and you behave as if all this were quite natural. A wealth of knowledge and power like that is something I can hardly understand."

Frabato looked at the professor seriously and replied, "Any human being can acquire knowledge and power of this kind as long as he can muster the energy to follow the path of magic up to the highest levels. This power was not simply *given* to me. In principle, I can use my energy and power freely, but I must be able to justify my deeds before Divine Providence. Since every high initiate is free from karma, he will avoid applying his magical powers for his own well-being. During any physical incarnation he is ordinarily allowed to exercise only those abilities that any common man has at his disposal. This is a law of development which must not be violated without special reason. The true magician knows that he is always united with Divine Providence in a way which is never given to any black magician. Through his deeds the black magician condemns himself to loneliness in the cosmos, unless he has a liking for demonic beings. The final damnation of a black magician in this case is incomprehensible to a normal person, for the feeling of utter loneliness can only be understood by an initiate.

"Because we initiates observe the positive spiritual laws to their final consequences, we are allowed to participate in the power of Divine Providence. This steadfast observance of the spiritual laws does not arise from the fear of possible

112

punishment by the karmic powers; rather, it is derived from the greatest absolute veneration of and humility towards the power and wisdom of Divine Providence of which a human being is capable. Reverence and humility are among the most important characteristics of the path of magic.

"The destiny of an initiate cannot ordinarily be understood by the immature and the uninitiated. This is due simply to a lack of insight into the spiritual laws. Not everybody is as fortunate as you, for I was permitted to give you a few examples of magical power. Actually, it is of greater advantage if one becomes convinced of the activity and effect of beings and laws through self-study, because it is the knowledge one has acquired on one's own that leads to true belief. In magic, belief is gradually replaced by knowledge. First, the student has to accept the teachings of the initiates with belief alone; then he will convince himself, through his own efforts, that his belief was justified. This kind of belief, which is sustained by knowledge, is called 'manifested belief,' and it was preached by Christ when he said that true faith can move mountains."

Lightning illuminated the room, followed by a crash of thunder. Both men involuntarily looked outside. "You see," Frabato continued, "in spite of the fact that the barometric pressure is high, the elemental beings have followed my order and have brought rain and thunder. If you could use your spiritual eyes, you would see how the elements are set in motion by the entities in order to bring about a thunderstorm like this. You would see how they direct the electrical currents to cause the effects you are familiar with. For we clairvoyants, it is obvious what happens in cases such as this, whereas in your eyes it looks like a miracle. The unleashing of the elements is one of the smallest Kabbalistic secrets of the magic of nature. Now what is left for me to do is to calm down the elements once again; otherwise, the thunderstorm will go on till tomorrow morning and cause a lot of damage."

Frabato now stood at the window. His eyes looked into the far distance as he murmured a few formulas which the professor did not understand. After a few minutes it stopped raining, the clouds parted slowly, the starry heavens became visible, and nature seemed to breathe again, refreshed. Quite relieved, Professor G. could now put on his dry clothes again. Frabato bade the professor farewell. The events of the day had left a deep impression on the professor and given him much food for thought.

*

In the weeks and months that followed, Frabato was very busy. The articles he had published in various magazines under a pseudonym fell on fertile ground. He made many new acquaintances and his metaphysical work brought him professional standing and authority. Of course there were also people who envied him, even hated him. Frabato had all kinds of enemies, but he just ignored them, leaving them completely to the powers of karma.

In the course of time he also made many contacts in other countries which brought him numerous invitations from all over the world. Therefore, one day Frabato decided to leave K.'s country house for an indefinite time to journey around the world. Preparations were quickly made and soon he was on his way. He traveled to the largest and most interesting cities, where, depending on the situation, he either worked as an initiate or as a teacher of spiritual sciences. Several years passed before Frabato returned.

There had been a number of changes during his absence. K. had married — in fact, he had made a marriage pact with a being of the water element. The affair did not end happily. K. had evoked an undine, but because he did not yet possess complete magical equilibrium, the bewitchingly beautiful water-being persuaded him to make a pact with her, one which he could not resist. The undine incarnated herself in the body of a beautiful young girl who was lying on her death bed, then cured the ailing body by magic and married K. Frabato had emphatically warned K. against pacts like this during their former meetings. He could see K.'s future clairvoyantly and knew the danger he was facing. Unfortunately, K. had not taken Frabato's warning seriously and thus had become a victim of the undine's seductive arts.

Helen, K.'s younger sister, married an industrialist from another country and became the mother of two children. The country house in the suburbs had changed its owner, too.

Frabato felt that his old associations had fallen away, and therefore decided to return to his home town. He had become tired of traveling around the world and wanted to create a more tranquil future. In his native town he established a new home and led a life of seclusion for the next couple of years.

Materialism and political fanaticism gained the upper hand in Europe. All those who took an interest in the spiritual and occult sciences were in great danger. The horrors of war seized millions of people for many years.

Chapter X

The moon shone clearly and gently through the window of Frabato's study, illuminating his figure as he sat motionless, absorbed in meditation. Though he was in a state of ecstasy, Frabato clearly perceived that he was being summoned spiritually by his secret name, known only to the Brothers of Light; and he therefore knew that he was being called to a meeting of the highest initiates.

The Brotherhood of Light is a spiritual organization which consists of the highest initiates of our cosmic system. Only one who has mastered and is able to practice the first three leaves of the Book of Wisdom has access to this brotherhood. Since the beginning of human spiritual evolution, those who have achieved the highest state of magical perfection and have not yet consciously dissolved their individuality are to be found in this organization. The Brothers of Light assume responsibility for the well-being and development of humankind, though the task of maintaining that development may not always require physical incarnation. The Brotherhood of Light is structured in accordance with a hierarchy which corresponds to the initiated members' degree of perfection. Their superior is the so-called Prime Initiator who has a rank equal to a Mahatma, the Deputy of Divine Order and the Custodian of All Secrets. In the hierarchy he is called Urgaya, the Wise Man of the Mountain or the Old Master. He has been the Prime Initiator since the beginning of the world, but rarely manifests himself. He customarily takes on a form only for very short periods of time when he chooses to stand by and give advice to a Brother of Light regarding his task.

In the hierarchy, the Old Master has twelve subordinate

adepts who have reached the highest spiritual perfection. These adepts take over the most difficult tasks, but they too are very seldom incarnate; therefore they usually do their work through the zone which girdles the earth. Some of these adepts are only incarnated once in a hundred or a thousand years. Urgaya and the twelve adepts form the Council of Elders and meet regularly or have special meetings to make important decisions concerning the fate of the peoples of the earth.

The twelve adepts have seventy-two wise men, or enlightened people under them, who again have 360 masters. The seventy-two wise men and the 360 masters are also summoned to a general assembly. In the case of special meetings, Urgaya sends for particular initiates.

When Frabato heard the call that evening, he knew there would be a general assembly. He had already been to many such meetings, and therefore was aware that important decisions were to be made on the course of the development of humanity and the nations of the world. Which task would he be given this time?

The Brotherhood of Light has no permanent domicile on earth, although they maintain certain points of reference in the Orient.[4] At that time, several brothers had incarnated in the Orient and worked in the framework of their missions. The general assembly always met in a magical room, created especially for that purpose in the zone girdling the earth. Urgaya always created this magical room personally, protecting it and making it visible only to the Brothers of Light, so that he would not be perceived, either spiritually or astrally, by alien beings.

---

[4] There is a correspondence between the astral and terrestrial geography which manifests itself in power points or points of entry or exit in various parts of the globe.

Frabato left his physical body both spiritually and astrally; it lay upon his bed pale and rigid. His breathing and heartbeat had ceased. With his spiritual and astral right hand Frabato made a magic circle around his physical body, uttering a protective Kabbalistic formula to protect it, for he knew full well that the slightest touch by another person would cause his physical death. The power of the Kabbalistic formula, on the other hand, yielded complete protection in all three spheres.

Moved by his power of imagination, he was in the temple of the Brothers of Light the next moment, for in the spiritual and astral worlds one can overcome any distance without loss of time; these worlds are ruled by timelessness.

Most of the brethren had already assembled in the holy temple of the Brothers of Light and had taken their usual seats. Judging by the astral bodies, every nation and race was represented. Urgaya sat in front of everyone in indescribable magnificence. His astral body was illuminated like liquid gold, his eyes sparkling like diamonds. There was no one there who was not permeated with the feeling that incarnate divinity was among them.

The interior of the temple symbolized the supreme wisdom of the cosmos. There were no windows, but twelve invisible chandeliers spread a radiant light which was by no means inferior to sunlight. The ceiling of the temple rested on twenty-two columns, symbolizing the Book of Wisdom. Each column radiated a special light which indicated its invisible power and significance. The ceiling alternately emanated a golden yellow and violet color, and was covered with thousands of stars.

Frabato had taken his seat and the last brethren had arrived. The assembly could now begin. Though the Old Master had remained motionless until now, he suddenly came to life. He scanned the room with inquiring eyes and nodded with satisfaction when he saw that all were present. Everyone, regardless of rank, stood and bowed in adoration before him. Urgaya thanked them with a gesture of blessing. The temple was filled with a blissful atmosphere. There was silence and expectation among the brothers. Urgaya opened the assembly in a calm voice:

"My dear brethren, admirers of light, supporters of everything good, who serve Divine Providence out of love and veneration, I welcome you cordially to this assembly. All of us who are gathered here have pledged to uphold the laws of Divine Providence for all eternity and to keep the Mysteries. We all are part of the Divine Light, before whom we bow in deepest humility and greatest veneration. The Light of Eternity unites us all. Omnipotence and wisdom have been given to us through divine grace and mercy. The omnipresent love of Divine Providence has joined us in an inseparable union. We are the Brothers of Light, Truth, and Life."

Those present had the impression that God Himself had spoken, for the temple was filled with an atmosphere of indescribable bliss which each experienced differently, according to his rank and maturity. Here, paradise had become reality. Here the highest ecstasy prevailed, and true connection to the Divine Light. No immature or uninitiated person could linger in this concentrated light. The initiates and magicians that had assembled had their true home here. The Apostle Paul's words found their meaning here: "But as it is written, the eye hath not seen nor ear heard, neither have entered into the heart of man the things which God hath prepared for them that love Him." Time and space seemed to have disappeared, and thousands of years — or perhaps only seconds — of earth time might have elapsed. This state of union with God cannot be comprehended by an untrained human being and cannot be described in words.

Urgaya, who had closed his eyes for a few moments, once again surveyed the assembly and changed the atmosphere in the temple.

"Dear brothers," he continued, "a few years of earthly time have passed since last we met here. As commissioned by Divine Providence, each of you who voluntarily co-operated in the great task of cosmic development was given an assignment by me. I am very pleased that each of you has loyally accomplished the task allotted him or else is still busy with his mission. I thank you from the depths of my heart and in the name of Divine Providence for all the effort and sacrifices you have made while working on this great mission. May the blessing of Divine Providence continue to be with all of you who work in humility and adoration to spread Divine Light.

"I have called you here because I want to distribute, in the name of Divine Providence, the new tasks for the coming era. The world is facing a difficult future, for the misuse of power will cast entire nations into disaster. It will be your task to ensure a certain equilibrium — while at the same time remaining within the confines of universal law. Your missions are difficult and will demand hard work from each and every one of you. May Divine Providence grant you the necessary strength to accomplish them!"

Seldom had Urgaya spoken with such serious intent, and everyone understood that the world was indeed facing power-ful historical events. Each of the Brothers knew that a part of the responsibility for the development of humankind would rest upon his shoulders. Yet the assembled initiates regarded it as a special honor to be allowed to participate in the great work of cosmic development, and each of them would of course exert all of his energy to accomplish his allotted task.

"My dear brothers," Urgaya continued in a serious tone, "as you know, light cannot exist without darkness and truth cannot exist without falsehood. According to the universal laws, the negative principle thus has the same right to exist as does the positive principle. Due to the development of science, the negative principle will gain great power over the peoples of the earth in the near future. Therefore, with the positive principle behind you, it will be your primary task to spread love and fraternity among humankind. While thus engaged, you must of course continue to observe the laws of karma, for good and evil alike are necessary for the unrestrained evolution of the human spirit. As you all know, wars represent a permanent condition on the earth and are caused by the polarity of light and darkness. But wars like the ones that will shock the planet in the near future have never taken place thus far in the history of the world. The extent of the destruction will exceed the boldest fantasies of men, and we certainly hope that those who survive will draw from this experience the necessary lessons and awaken better equipped against any future temptations."

At these words, the assembly contemplated sadly the destiny of the nations, for they were able to image a vivid picture of what humanity was sure to face. Those who were allowed to partake in the harmony of the Divine Light were, however, determined to help all those who aspired to realize positive goals.

Frabato, who for thousands of years had been entering into incarnation only to help humankind in its spiritual development, had witnessed wars and annihilation throughout the course of world history; he understood the seriousness of Urgaya's words and that they must have a ponderable significance.

What task would he be asked to fulfill this time? "May Divine Providence grant me steadfastness," he thought to himself.

As a complete being, he could of course dissolve himself into the universal Divine Light at any time — but that would mean the final loss of his individuality. Apart from that, his mission would then have to be taken over by the other brothers.

Frabato enjoyed the highest confidence among the Brothers of Light. Depending on what sort of task he was given, he was often allowed to make use of the greatest magical abilities. Thinking of the bright but remote future of humankind, he was determined to contribute to its development, no matter how great the difficulties.

Urgaya now began to distribute the missions for the next period of development. He beckoned everyone to approach him and informed each of his new mission. There were tasks of various kinds and difficulties, depending on the nation or country wherein the initiate would work, and what Divine Providence deemed to be of special importance there.

First the 360 masters were given their tasks. Then Urgaya summoned the seventy-two enlightened initiates, all of whom were entrusted with especially difficult challenges. Much to his own amazement, Frabato, who was first in rank among those seventy-two initiates, was not called upon when his turn came. Without hesitation, Urgaya continued to distribute tasks among the twelve adepts who, without exception, received the most difficult tasks.

Frabato was surprised and concerned. What was this supposed to mean? He had been completely overlooked during the distribution of tasks. Was he no longer to receive a mission? Though he had sometimes grown weary of life, he had always fulfilled his tasks. What was to be done with him this time?

As these questions occupied his mind, the last of the twelve adepts was given an assignment. At last Urgaya looked upon Frabato and beckoned him to approach. Before Frabato could fall to his knees before the representative of Divine Providence, Urgaya stood and placed his hands upon Frabato's head, saying:

"Brother of Light, I bless you. You need not worry, for Divine Providence loves you and appreciates your co-operation. You have been serving the Light for thousands of years. You are free to dissolve your individuality any time you want, but I believe we would all regard this as a great loss to the future, for not one of those present has been incarnated on earth as often as you.

"Planet Earth is facing difficult times and destinies, and no one is better acquainted with its inhabitants than you are. Frabato, I am convinced that you will complete your present incarnation well, including the task associated with it, though it is one of your most difficult."

A special distinction of this nature had not been bestowed upon an initiate for hundreds of years. Greatly astonished, Frabato sank to his knees before Urgaya and bowed deeply.

"I will no longer think of dissolving my individuality and will go on serving Divine Providence loyally," he thought as though expressing an oath.

Urgaya asked Frabato to sit down before him and then went back to his exalted seat. From there he addressed the assembly once again:

"Brothers of Light! As you know, science has made great advances. The speed of technical progress will continue to increase tremendously during this century, and, because of this development, man will procure mighty weapons. The danger is that these weapons may be used negatively by those responsible, whereby the spiritual development of entire nations may of course be influenced. Through our activities, a counterweight is to be created against these negative forces. Today one of our brothers has been given the task of inspiring leading individual personalities to apply such technical inventions towards peace and the well-being of humankind."

An initiate with profound eyes nodded, for it was he who had been allotted this task.

"Dear Frabato," Urgaya said, "the negative tendencies in the advancement of humankind cannot be ignored. The world's materialistic ideology has already seized a large part of humanity and will continue to grow. As a consequence, there will be an ever increasing drive for money, profit, and power, as well as for the satisfaction of the lower passions. During the days of Atlantis you experienced for yourself what materialistic thinking and irresponsible actions can lead to."

Frabato nodded, for he remembered the fall of Atlantis very well. In the course of a technical experiment which was carried out by irresponsible scientists possessed by the notion of "progress," the axis of the earth had lost its equilibrium, which consequently brought about the destruction of Atlantis within a short time — the details of the drama are indelibly recorded in the Akasha, where every good initiate may obtain a clear picture of the entire history of the cosmos.

Frabato still did not know any details regarding his future mission. The brothers were usually informed of their tasks with a few explanatory words. They were not accustomed to such long prologues; therefore a distinct suspense was now perceptible amongst those present.

"The whole endeavor of science is directed towards exploring the secrets of matter," Urgaya continued, "and thus it places its confidence entirely in the application of physical and chemical laws. This confidence in the effectiveness of technical means has resulted in the belief, at least among the majority, that the spiritual entities who stand behind the whole matter are non-existent. Only the initiates know that there is a spiritual science. The only tools this science employs for its research are human nature and human power. This science is the science of magic, which has existed since the beginning. You are all acquainted with the laws of magic, and you know that, despite all your freedom, you are only allowed to make use of the power of this science within the limits of Divine Law. Brother Christ expressed this concept by saying: 'I have not come into this world to change the laws but to fulfill them.' I ask you, from the depths of my heart, always to follow the spiritual laws accordingly."

Urgaya glanced at Frabato, who nodded his head repentantly, for he knew that these words were intended especially for him. He had now and again intervened to halt the darker powers when it was still permitted to do so by the laws of the karma. He had most often been unable to resist this temptation where the need to combat so-called black magic was concerned.

Urgaya saw that his words had had the intended effect and therefore considered the matter settled. Again he spoke to Frabato:

"Magic has, until the present day, been a secret knowledge. The true spiritual laws have been accessible only to very special circles, who in turn have passed them on only to those of their students who have passed difficult examinations. This manner of dissemination has had the advantage that the majority of people have been exempted thereby from the temptation of applying magical means in negative ways. On the other hand, there has been a disadvantage in that the people who have had no access to magical circles have no knowledge of the path from belief to knowledge, and consequently have never been able to proceed along this path.

"The armed conflicts of the past have brought death to millions of people. Many of these departed human beings have complained in the spiritual world that the true ways of spiritual development have never been accessible to them. It is now your task, dear brother, to reveal to humankind the true initiation into Hermetics by publishing appropriate material."

Somewhat shocked, Frabato stared at Urgaya, but, before he could answer, Urgaya had risen from his seat and motioned him to his side. Frabato went with him to the first pillar of the hall, where Urgaya said calmly and decidedly:

"Frabato, you know that this pillar symbolizes the first page of the Book of Wisdom. You shall publish the secrets of this first page, completely unveiled and without the use of symbols. Show humankind how to proceed from belief to knowledge."

Then Urgaya led Frabato, deeply moved, to the second pillar and, pointing to it with his hand, told him that the secrets of the second page of the Book of Wisdom were to be made accessible as well.

Of course, Frabato knew that the second pillar was the key to the magic of the spheres and contained the secrets of their hierarchy. He hoped that Urgaya would not go any further, but the latter, unperturbed, turned his steps toward the third pillar, symbolizing the creative word, and said to Frabato:

"'In the beginning was the Word'. It is so difficult for people to understand this when they have no knowledge of the divine language. For this reason you shall also reveal the secrets of the third page of Wisdom."

Then he led Frabato to the fourth pillar, touched it slightly with his hand, and said, "The fourth page of the Book of Wisdom shall be explained to humankind."

Having arrived at the fifth pillar he said: "Here, with the fifth pillar, your task shall come to an end. You will only be allowed to reveal the front side of this page. You do understand why, do you not?"

Side by side, they returned from whence they came. Urgaya sat down again; he seemed to be waiting for Frabato to say something about his new mission.

In the meantime, Frabato had become aware of the far-reaching implications of his task. He dropped to his knees and raised his eyes to Urgaya, beseechingly:

"Magnificent representative of Divine Providence, custodian of all cosmic secrets! I implore you from the bottom of my heart to release me from this duty! When you

127

called me last, I loyally accomplished the mission with which I was charged. According to your wishes I was incarnated into the body of a fourteen-year-old boy in order to become his father's spiritual teacher. Furthermore, I traveled the world in order to give evidence to humankind of the existence of the spiritual world. With your benevolent permission I was allowed to make use of my magical abilities to attest to the divine omnipotence, to heal the sick, and to reveal the future. Most reverend Master, you know that in principle no task is too difficult for me, but I beg you to take into consideration my special situation. I have been serving you and Divine Providence as an initiate for thousands of years. In hidden temples I passed on the secret teachings only to the most mature students, and I obeyed the laws strictly and mercilessly and executed anyone who transgressed against them, as the laws dictated in the old days. As a priest of the temple, I carried out initiations under severe oaths. How can I now disclose the Holy Mysteries to immature men? I have always been especially devoted to silence. How can I now cast pearls before swine and set free that light which will burn all those who are not mature? Surely people are not yet sufficiently developed to receive these teachings. They will drag divine wisdom into the mud; they will misunderstand it and dishonor it! I beseech you to deliver me from this task and to give me another."

It was a rare occasion for any adept or initiate to try and reject the task allotted to him. If an exchange was not possible amongst the brothers, a number of them would usually take up the task in addition to their own. Urgaya now addressed the assembly with serious intent:

"My dear brothers, you have heard what Frabato has been asked to do. Is there one among you who would like to exchange his task for Frabato's?"

Urgaya looked inquiringly at the assembly of initiates, but there was no answer. The question preyed on the minds of the

Franz Bardon

Franz Bardon

Franz Bardon

Franz Bardon

Hermes Trismegistos

Lao-tse

Mahum Tah-Ta
Initiator And Original Master
Of The Blue Monks

The Temple Of Shambalah

Brothers of Light while Urgaya waited motionless for a few moments longer. Then he looked at Frabato, kindly saying:

"My dear brother, your task is difficult and I do understand your objections. Its implementation, however, was ordered by God for the coming time period; therefore it will have to be carried out under any circumstances. Since you have almost always been a teacher in your many incarnations and, without doubt, have always been one of the most capable of all the brothers in this respect, I have chosen you for this mission. You will be able to find the correct words in order to explain to humankind the true laws of harmony and development towards perfection. Many of the brothers present began with the path of saintliness because they did not have a personal teacher and lacked the necessary knowledge about the true magical paths. As you see, no one here is prepared to accept your task; therefore I kindly ask you to carry out this mission for the benefit of human evolution and to reveal the divine wisdom."

In the meantime Frabato had begun to see the great necessity of his task, and, though he was aware of the fact that there would be great obstacles to overcome, he felt reassured and strengthened by Urgaya's words.

"Honorable Master," he replied, bowing, "I shall try to carry out this task as best I can."

After these words a sigh of relief seemed to pass through the assembly, for no one would have been pleased to take over this additional task.

Frabato wanted to return to his seat but Urgaya motioned him to remain with him. After a few moments Urgaya's face became transfigured. An extraordinary phosphorescence illuminated his astral body, which grew more and more transparent and ethereal.

Frabato knew that Urgaya was capable of realizing the highest state of bliss and unification with Divine Providence in his astral body. And, as if from a far distance, words which were not Urgaya's sounded from the deepest innermost of the incomprehensible light:

"Frabato, you are my loyal son and I love you. I am pleased that you have accepted this task of publishing the true magical initiation, although you are also burdened with a difficult karma. It is well-known to you that those whose development is one-sided will only be able to realize a part of My being within themselves. It is my wish that everyone be given the opportunity to proceed along the path to perfection. It must be possible for everyone to understand My being and to obtain the knowledge of how, with the universal laws, I created the world. Every human being must continue to be reincarnated here on earth until he has achieved complete magical equilibrium within himself."

As these words were spoken many of the brothers remembered their own past, and how they had first traveled along the indirect path of saintliness, thus developing in a one-sided manner and being obliged, through successive incarnations, to make up for what they lacked. Only those who had been guided by a magician had been able to take the direct way to perfection.

God's voice continued to speak through Urgaya: "To accomplish your task it is not advisable for you to work miracles in public. From now on you shall no longer demonstrate your magical abilities in order to convince people of the existence of higher powers and laws. When you return to your body, you must change your strategy, and you will no doubt succeed in doing so. I appreciate your work very much. In making My laws public, you do not dishonor Me; rather, you will be showing humankind the true path to Me. Every human being should be given the opportunity to start on the way to initiation, to true, genuine perfection, beginning from wherever his fate has put him.

"For the remainder of your present life you are not to behave in any way like an initiate, and you may use any means to disguise yourself when necessary so that no one will know. Acquire all medical knowledge necessary so that there will be no difference between you and a professional physician. Healing through the Word will only cause attention and will make you unnecessary enemies. You may, however, make use of the laws of the fifth pillar, the fifth page of the Book of Wisdom, of alchemy, when healing people.

"You are aware of the fact that the greater the mission, the greater will be the resistance from the negative powers. They cannot attack you spiritually, but due to the karma of this physical body which you have accepted, you will have to face worries, sorrows, and misery. Many enemies will persecute you, many diseases will afflict you, and your life will often be in danger. The fate to which your earthly body is subjected will work against you, because the negative entities know that you are a Brother of Light, and they will attack you wherever there is an opportunity to do so. If you accomplish this task well, you will have made another great contribution to the development of humankind, and in the near future you will be able to perform your teaching duties exclusively in the spiritual world among highly developed students."

As these last words were fading, Urgaya's figure reassumed its original appearance. Frabato knew that Divine Providence had manifested itself and had spoken to him directly through Urgaya. He was filled with overwhelming joy and, full of confidence and energy for his future task, he thanked Divine Providence in a silent prayer of reverence, vowing to accomplish his task loyally, no matter how great the obstacles might be.

Urgaya looked at Frabato with sincerity and, with a gesture of blessing, asked him to take his seat among the brothers. Then Urgaya arose and lifted his hands to bless the assembly of initiates, and said:

"Be blessed in the name of Divine Providence for your

voluntary assistance in the great work of human and cosmic development. I am pleased that all of you have proven to be true sons of God. I thank you and hereby close the assembly."

A short time later the Brothers of Light left the temple, and Urgaya, who had created it with the manifested power of his imagination, dissolved his work again and retired into impenetrable and inaccessible regions.

Chapter XI

Frabato returned to his earthly body, though any sleep was understandably impossible after such a meeting. The day was dawning and Frabato realized that he had been away for several hours. The events of the assembly remained strongly imprinted in his mind.

In the days that followed, he remained deeply concerned about his new mission, and it became very difficult for him to concentrate on his daily routine. Following the advice of Divine Providence, he soon began an intensive study of medicine — though he also had to earn a living.

After completing his studies, he devoted himself entirely to the healing arts, and soon had a good reputation as a diagnostician and naturopath.

He hoped that the writing of the Book of Wisdom would be postponed for an indefinite time, for the occult sciences were facing very difficult days. Fearful that their own underhanded dealings would be brought out into the open and opposed, the heads of state cruelly persecuted supporters and practitioners of the occult sciences, as well as those who wrote on the subject. Lodges and metaphysical societies were dissolved and many of their members persecuted, arrested, and executed. Frabato, who was not unknown in occult circles, suffered greatly under this increasing oppression. Unfortunately, the physical body he had assumed was burdened with a heavy karma. Like so many others, he was pulled into the escalating hellish inferno. Sent to a concentration camp for three years, he shared the fate of hundreds of thousands. Because he refused to place his magical abilities at the disposal of the heads of state, he was exposed to great humiliation and cruel tortures, which he endured with undaunted steadfastness. With devastating power, the war — the likes of which the world had seldom experienced before — raged on for six years.

Shortly before the end of the war, Frabato was sentenced to death, but the concentration camp in which he was incarcerated was bombed before the sentence could be carried out. Frabato was freed by some of his fellow prisoners and escaped. Divine Providence had protected him and kept him alive. Robbed of everything, marked with disease but freed from the chains of prison, Frabato returned to his home country.

After convalescing for a while, he at once started to work for his suffering fellow man by using his extensive medical knowledge. Many people went to see him — especially those deemed incurable by traditional medicine — and he was able to heal them, either partly or completely, depending on what was still possible within the parameters of their own karma. When it was sometimes too late to rescue the earthly shell, he could only give consolation with psychological therapy. It was due to his extraordinarily successful treatments that the number of people who came to him for help grew steadily, so that in the end he limited his practice exclusively to those who were genuinely suffering.

*

One night after a strenuous day, Frabato sought a few hours of sleep for his body. But then Urgaya called him by his spiritual name.

"What does this mean?" Frabato thought. "This is not a meeting day. Perhaps I am to be reminded of my duties."

Without hesitation, he separated himself spiritually and astrally from his physical body and, after having protected the latter against demonic influences, he appeared before Urgaya the very next moment.

Frabato greeted the head of the Brothers of Light with a deep bow, and Urgaya, sitting cross-legged on a small carpet in a grotto, responded with a gesture of blessing. Frabato was alone with him. The surroundings were illuminated only by a very dim light. The grotto was situated at the foot of a high mountain, but any being of the cosmos who sought to find it would search in vain, for Urgaya had made it visible only to those he wanted to see.

"You are welcome, Frabato. Please sit down beside me," Urgaya said, beckoning to a second carpet. Frabato thanked him and did as he was requested. They spent a few minutes in silent prayer in honor of Divine Providence, as was customary with the Brothers of Light whenever they met. Then Urgaya turned his shining eyes on Frabato, saying:

"This is not an official meeting, but only an encounter between the two of us. As you know, I only call for someone individually when I think that help is necessary to accomplish a task or when I have to reprimand someone. These, however, are not the reasons for my calling you. It is something else. I have to thank you, in the name of Divine Providence and the Brothers of Light, for your steadfastness and loyalty, and especially for your observance of karmic law during the recent tragic military conflicts. Divine Providence watches over you and protects you.

"One member of the Group of Twelve has dissolved his individuality after accomplishing his mission and has returned to the Primordial Light. His position has thus become vacant, and Divine Providence has authorized me to transfer it to you. This means that you have been admitted to the Council of Elders, and from now on you, like the other eleven brothers, will occupy the highest rank a human being can achieve in the hierarchy of initiates. Of course, you also accept all the obligations that are due to the Light. There is no turning back for you. You may choose freely whether you wish to relinquish your individuality and dissolve yourself in the

Primordial Light. However, Divine Providence hopes that you will continue to work within the scope of cosmic development. I am very pleased that you are now irrevocably connected with Divine Providence and that I have been the one to give you the news."

Urgaya's words filled Frabato with great emotion and joy, for acceptance to the Council of Elders was the highest possible distinction.

"Sublime Master," Frabato answered, "I thank you for this news. I am deeply moved that God has considered me worthy to be accepted into the Council of Elders. It has always been an honor for me to put my energy at the disposal of Divine Providence. The progress of human development has always been my special interest."

Urgaya nodded benevolently and replied: "My dear brother, I expected you to say this. Of all our brothers, you are among the most mature, and I am pleased that you intend to serve humankind as an example in the future as well. Surely you remember that you have been given the task of revealing the first five pages of the Book of Wisdom? The time has now come for this task to be realized. This is one of the reasons we are meeting, and I must ask you to attach great importance to it."

Frabato's silent hope that Divine Providence might for some reason release him from his task was now dashed. There was no way out: this difficult assignment must be accomplished.

Urgaya noticed that there was still some resistance on Frabato's part. Therefore, he tried to explain the matter once more:

"Dear Frabato," he said, "the last disastrous world war and the other current wars on earth have, during the last few years, sent millions of people into the beyond, the zone girdling the earth, and once again there have been many among them who, during their stay on earth, were never

136

given the opportunity to learn the true laws of initiation. They have raised serious complaints in the spiritual world, arguing that fate alone served as their teacher, for the path to human freedom had been kept secret. Finally, to put an end to the accusations, Divine Providence chose you to introduce, to all those who love the truth and seek wisdom, the true spiritual sciences through a corresponding literature. Though the negative forces will continue to put severe obstacles in your way, I trust that Divine Providence will always give you the support necessary to publish these mysteries. Be inspired always with the desire to show your fellow man the way to true perfection."

"Honorable Master," Frabato tried to object, "when I publish the mysteries of magic my true identity cannot be concealed from people. Many who read my books will sooner or later discover that I belong to another level of development. They will want me to give evidence of my art. They will come to me with their material concerns and will ask me to arrange matters favorably in accordance with their wishes. Sublime Master, it was you yourself who, during our last meeting, imposed upon me the duty of keeping my spiritual maturity a secret by any means. How am I to conceal my identity when I am asked to reveal the secret mysteries?"

Urgaya seemed to have been anticipating the question, for he answered with a delicate smile:

"My dear brother, as far as I know you have managed quite well with every being you have encountered in our cosmos over thousands of years. Therefore, I am convinced that your knowledge of methods and appropriate behavior is sufficient, and I need not give you any detailed advice. Through the publication of the path of magic, people will assume that you are an initiate, and you need not deny this fact to your readers. You must not consider this a breach of silence, but as part of your mission. Divine Providence will send you the people whom you really should help. You will, no doubt, find the right words for the curious and the sensation seekers. You will show those who are unafraid of knowledge the right way to educate themselves so as to be able to cope with any situation that is part of their destiny. You should not use your magical abilities to convince people: those who need to be convinced in order to believe are not yet sufficiently mature for the path of magic. Such people are incapable of taking the reins of their fate into their own hands with their own power, and therefore they still need fate for a teacher. On the other hand, there will also be those of serious intent who are striving for truth, and they will come to you for advice. You will certainly not refuse them your help when they question you concerning their own spiritual development.

"Dear Frabato, even if only a few people on earth should now succeed in achieving the necessary maturity for initiation through diligence, endurance, and hard work, your task will have been accomplished. Those who merely enrich their intellectual knowledge through your writings and decide to remain with theory alone in their present incarnation will be given the opportunity to begin the practical work during their next lifetime.

"Your writings will find their way over the entire world. With time, seekers of truth and wisdom will become familiar with them. However, no one will be able to harvest the fruits of wisdom without a serious search, and Divine Providence will see to it that those who are mature enough to understand the content of these writings will in fact receive them. Then the complaints of the deceased in the zone girdling the earth will cease, because no one will be able to assert that the path to the spiritual world was not accessible to him."

Urgaya's impressive words had made the necessity of his task clear to Frabato once again. "Sublime Master," he addressed Urgaya, "what you have just said has convinced me completely and definitely, and I shall carry out my task loyally. May Divine Providence protect the mysteries, for I am only fulfilling your request."

Urgaya thanked Frabato, gave him a few more instructions concerning his mission, and then dismissed him with a blessing. Frabato said farewell to the chief of the Brotherhood of Light by bowing deeply, and then disappeared from the grotto.

Having returned to his physical body, sleep was the farthest thing from his mind as he thought for a long time about how to implement his mission.

He began to make his task manifest soon thereafter. Fully confident in Divine Providence, he carried out his assignment to the best of his knowledge and belief. Written in common language, divine wisdom found its way into the world, illuminating the way especially for those whose longing for true knowledge is great and who have realized that the paths to spiritual perfection have indeed been revealed to them through Frabato's writings.

The End

Epilogue

I have portrayed the life of an initiate in the form of a novel. He who can read between the lines will recognize valuable, practical, and scientific concepts in some of the chapters.

This novel demonstrates the effects of good and evil. The important thing is: everything in this story is true. All the events related herein serve to instruct the reader, in an entertaining manner, that he ought not to think of everyone who is unfriendly, or who does not think good thoughts, or who threatens his reputation as being a black magician. The disadvantages of destiny cannot always be attributed to the effects of black magic.

For the sake of information, let it be said that a true black magician is interested only in those who are spiritually highly evolved, and who have attained a certain level of esoteric development. Black magicians turn their attention only to such individuals, and attempt to influence them in some way. The black magician is never concerned with trifles — for example, making a cow unable to produce milk. Only those who have little or no knowledge in this area of esoteric studies entertain such superstitions.

By the same token, this book is not meant to be an advertisement for any association or lodge which, through exotic and abstract names, tries to obtain ignorant members who, consequently, become victims of constant oppression. I shall refrain here from naming any lodges which do not teach the true sciences.

The Brothers of Light concerning whom I have written in this book are not a worldly organization and do not have a residence on earth. They constitute an association of mature souls who meet only in the super-terrestrial zones.

Anyone who has mastered the practice of the first three pages of the Book of Wisdom may enter this Brotherhood. Whoever has achieved this level draws the attention of the Brothers of Light to himself effortlessly.

I sincerely wish all the very best to those who are interested in and possess my books.

The Author

In Memoriam

Although the following information will sadden the interested reader, I consider it my duty to inform the public that Franz Bardon is no longer with us in the physical body. On July 10th, 1958, Divine Providence allowed his perfected spirit to leave the earthly shell of the body which had served for his mission. Master Bardon left his body forever under unusual circumstances, as have so many high initiates on earth.

It is known to but a few that a high initiate such as Franz Bardon does not endure the entire normal development of an incarnation, as do the other inhabitants of earth. His is a perfect spirit, and he needs to accept a human form only when Divine Providence entrusts him with a new mission. In order to convey a rough idea of such a spirit to the reader, I will give a brief account of the author's life as far as I am informed about it.

Franz Bardon mentions, in his novel *Frabato,* that he had embodied himself in the body of a fourteen-year-old boy in order to become the spiritual teacher of the boy's father, Viktor Bardon. Viktor Bardon was engaged in Christian mysticism and, owing to his persistence and piety, he later advanced to the level of clairvoyance. But despite his clairvoyance, he could not achieve the goal that he longed for so much — he could not reach his spiritual goal of becoming more closely connected with God, because he lacked further relevant training in the field. Therefore he included in his fervent prayers the sublime wish that he might meet a true guru during his present incarnation, in order to hear his teachings and accept them.

His noble yearning did not remain unfulfilled. Frabato's

spirit was embodied in the only son that Viktor Bardon had (in addition to his twelve daughters), and, as the oldest child, he was to become his father's true guru, quite apart from the mission that Divine Providence had assigned to him. When this wonderful exchange took place one night, no one except the clairvoyant Viktor Bardon noticed, and he thanked God sincerely for this blessing. From that day on he had a personal guru in his own son and appreciated this very much.

Only a perfect and high initiate like the spirit of Franz Bardon can dare to and succeed in doing something like this — borrowing a body to complete not just one mission, but a number of them. The choice and acceptance of a body which has already reached puberty is subject to a number of conditions; i.e. as compensation, its new inhabitant must allot another and more favorable existence to the original owner, somewhere in a mother's womb. Besides this, the initiate must accept the borrowed body's karma as his own, regardless of what that may be, and that karma must under all circumstances be equilibrated.

Because the karma of his body's original owner was heavily burdened, Franz Bardon, in spite of his spiritual perfection and high adepthood, had to endure much before being able to correct it. To mention a few examples for the reader's information, I should like to point out his numerous struggles for existence, his numerous arrests and his three and a half years in a concentration camp — during which he had to endure the most cruel and bitter events and the greatest humiliations of his life. Also, the last few months of his life were overshadowed by extremely unpleasant circumstances which finally put an end to his blessed work. The acceptance of such an incarnation should be the greatest proof for all of us regarding the generosity of Franz Bardon's spirit in remaining at all times in human form.

These brief accounts will make it clear to the reader why a great spirit, whose extraordinary abilities came close to the might of Divine Providence, nevertheless had to endure many unpleasant experiences, without wincing, although it was possible for him to render his persecutors instantly harmless with a mere gesture of his hand. It is the same with the fates of other human beings, wherein Divine Providence allows no one, not even an initiate or a chosen one, to interfere. Therefore it is only a matter of human ignorance when people describe the proceedings of destiny as unjust, and consider the true initiate an incapable human being simply because he loyally adheres to the commandments of Divine Providence and therefore does not wish to fulfill anyone's foolish desires.

I have refrained from describing the usual details of Franz Bardon's career such as his schooling, his vocation and his professional life, assuming that the account I have given is more important and instructive to the interested reader and student of Hermetic sciences. Those who had the good fortune to meet Franz Bardon personally know very well that one of our best has left us. True students of Hermetics still regard Franz Bardon as their great guru, whether he is in the flesh or not. His spiritual greatness is timeless. Those who are seriously and practically engaged in the scientific writings of Franz Bardon but who never met him personally or who only knew him for a very short time will get an idea of his spiritual greatness when I give them the names of a number of personalities from different ages whose physical bodies were inhabited by the same great spirit — by the spirit of Hermes Trismegistos whose Book of Wisdom, called Thoth, contains the seventy-eight Tarot cards, and who is certainly known to every occultist. Therefore, no one will be surprised by the leitmotiv that Mr. Bardon chose for his first book, *Initiation Into Hermetics*. Lao-tse, the Chinese sage and scientist, is also known to all philosophers; the same is true of the French astrologer Nostradamus, the English scholar Robert Fludd, and the Comte de Saint-Germain. We also find Franz Bardon's spirit in Apollonius of Tyana, a contemporary of Christ. In the incarnation before his last he was embodied in Tibet as Mahum Tah-Ta, the wise man of the mountains.

After Franz Bardon's physical departure, thousands of people all over the world missed their savior, advisor, and supporter in many moments of need. His dedicated and benevolent work deserves full recognition and appreciation and should always be remembered thankfully.

We who know that there is no such thing as death cherish the wish that Divine Providence may grant us the grace of meeting this high initiate, in whatever form or personage he may be embodied, during one of our future incarnations.

Prague, September 1958
Otti Votavova
(April 11, 1903 – February 9, 1973)

Fragments from

The Golden Book Of Wisdom

by
Franz Bardon

Contents of
The Golden Book of Wisdom

Introduction

The fourth page in the Book of Wisdom is the fourth Tarot card, which depicts a wise man or, sometimes, an emperor. The description of the fourth Tarot card is of very great assistance to magicians, spheric magicians and Kabbalists, for it allows them to penetrate more deeply into the secrets of wisdom and thereby enables them to solve the greatest problems. This is true not only from the point of view of knowledge but, more importantly, from the point of view of cognition, and thereby from the point of view of wisdom.

An initiate must be able to answer any question he may be asked at any time. If he has followed his path correctly, he must be capable of immediately solving any problem with which he may be faced regarding the universal laws. The theorist will also derive much from this book to enrich his theoretical knowledge, because he will be able to answer for himself many questions concerning those universal laws.

Logically, it is impossible to accommodate and explain wisdom in its entirety in a single book. A part of the universal wisdom, however, is contained in this work. Above all, the subject matter of my three preceding books[5] will be illuminated from many aspects. This book will help anyone who is seriously studying and practicing its contents to become more acquainted with the universal laws and their effects, whereby he will expand his consciousness and increase his knowledge. The more he identifies himself with

---

[5] *Initiation Into Hermetics, The Practice of Magical Evocation,* and *The Key to the True Kabbalah.*

the comprehensive subject matter, the more will he be fascinated by the greatness and power of these laws; and he will be filled with boundless awe, and will look up to Divine Providence with humility.

In the secret schools for prophets and priests of all ages, the fourth Tarot card, the Book of Wisdom, served as the fundamental subject matter which prepared the initiates for their high offices as instructors, initiators, and teachers (gurus). This book has thus been a work of initiation, revealing the deepest mysteries. The neophytes considered the Golden Book of Wisdom as an examination paper on their spiritual paths. Therefore, this fourth scientific work can, with good reason, be regarded as the foundation of esoteric Hermetics.

Thus far, the high mysteries symbolized by the fourth Tarot card have been passed on only in the language of symbols, and consequently they have usually remained obscure to the intellectual. The reader will no doubt appreciate the fact that, with the permission of Divine Providence, I have made an effort to translate the fourth book into the language of the intellect, in order to make it intelligible not only to the initiate but to the non-initiate, i.e. the philosopher and theorist, as well.

Anyone who completely masters this Book of Wisdom will have a thorough knowledge of the foundations of Hermetic philosophy, and may be considered a Hermetic philosopher from the standpoint of the universal laws. Also, the Hermetic brotherhoods and orders that teach the true Hermetic knowledge will class such a person with the philosophical practitioners.

If this fourth work is accepted with the same enthusiasm that greeted my three preceding books, then the description of the fourth Tarot card, which symbolically represents the Book of Wisdom, will also have done its job.

Therefore, may this book too be an inexhaustible,

ever-flowing source of knowledge and wisdom to the interested reader. May the blessing of Divine Providence accompany you all, to a high degree, on your path to perfection.

The Author

Chapter I
The Hermetic View of Religion

There are two basic philosophies of religion: the first is the relative and the second is the absolute or universal. From the beginning of humankind to the present day, all those religions which belong to the relative philosophy of religion have gone through their initial stages, have reached their peaks and, during the course of the ages, have come to their end. Each relative religion has its own founder. I refrain from citing all the systems of relative religion; anyone who has studied religious philosophy will have become acquainted with a number of religious systems of the relative type. They are all subject to the same law of transitoriness, regardless of whether they have lasted for hundreds or thousands of years. The length of time a religion may exist always depends upon its founders and teachers. The more universal laws a religion contains, the more universal truth it represents and preaches, the longer it lasts.

Its existence will be shorter the more one-sided, fanatical, dictatorial, and authoritarian its doctrines are. However, each religious system has thus far had its good purposes and its special mission. Each has always contained certain partial aspects, however concealed, of a portion of universal truth and lawfulness, whether symbolically or as an abstract idea.

A true adept will see in each relative religion, regardless of the historical era in which it may have existed, fragments of some basic ideas that had their origin in the universal religion and which point to universal law. Therefore, the adept appreciates each religion equally, without paying any attention to whether it is a religion of the past or whether it still exists today or whether it will exist in the future, because he is aware of the fact that each religious system has followers whose maturity suits that of the religion.

From the Hermetic point of view, even materialism is a kind of religious system, one whose representatives may believe in God but not in anything supernatural, and who adhere only to that of which they are able convince themselves — in other words, to them it is matter which prevails. Since the initiate knows that matter is the symbolic representation of the divine appearance reflected in the laws of nature, he will not judge anyone who believes merely in matter. The more mature a man has become during the course of his incarnations and evolution, the closer will he come to the universal laws, and the more deeply will he be able to penetrate into them, until finally no relative religious concept will satisfy him. A person like this has become mature for the universal religion and is capable of approaching the universal laws in the microcosm and macrocosm.

This is to say that any religion that does not represent the universal laws completely is relative and transitory. The universal laws have been unchangeable from the beginning of the world and will continue thus until the end.

The mature Hermetic may officially belong to any religion, depending on whether he really wants to do so and whether he considers it preferable in his dealings with people — perhaps to avoid drawing the attention of immature individuals to himself. However, in the innermost of his spirit and his entire being he will profess the universal religion, by which the universal lawfulness is to be understood. An initiate does not believe anything unless he can convince himself of its validity; neither does he believe in any personified divinity nor any kind of idol. Rather, he worships the universal law and harmony in all forms of existence.

These few words should suffice to demonstrate the difference between relative and absolute philosophies of religion.

Chapter II
Magic and Mysticism

Throughout the ages, magic and mysticism have been taught simultaneously and with equal emphasis in the secret schools for priests, for these two basic philosophical outlooks have always been extremely important in Hermetic science and will continue to be so in the future. Magic was once an integral part of all those sciences that developed in the course of time on the material plane and of everything which concerned this plane. Therefore all technical knowledge, no matter in which field of science, was passed on from master to student at the discretion of the priestly caste. All sciences, among them mathematics, chemistry, physics, and astronomy, were included in the field of magic.

On the other hand, everything insubstantial, such as religion, philosophy, the understanding of God, morality, virtues, abilities, and qualities of any kind fell within the scope of mysticism. Therefore, from the Hermetic point of view, magic cannot be separated from mysticism, because where there is no lawful, substantial material basis, neither can there be any abilities nor any virtues nor moral views.

With time and the development of humankind, the material sciences have isolated themselves in their own progress. By necessity they have become independent, since the higher inherent laws of energy, matter and substance — which could no longer be perceived with the coarse physical senses and for which a certain maturity was required for their comprehension — isolated themselves.

Consequently, two fields of knowledge developed. Firstly, the physical knowledge that one could acquire by intellectual training; and secondly, the metaphysical knowledge that dealt with the more subtle powers and substances, but which could not be comprehended by the mere intellect alone. This was the reason that metaphysical knowledge receded into the background and finally became the property of the true adepts alone. However, a Hermetic who is capable of penetrating the metaphysical laws must, according to those same laws, understand the logical connection between all existing branches of knowledge.

To avoid any confusion, I will not use the term "metaphysics" in my further explanations, but will stay with the term "magic," as the Hermetics did in former times. From the Hermetic point of view, magic is nothing else but a higher metaphysics that deals with powers, matters, and substances of a more subtle nature, but which has an analogous association with the general sciences of today, no matter to which branch of knowledge they may belong. Therefore, whenever an initiate speaks about magic, he is referring to powers, subtle matters and substances, their laws, their working effects in the microcosm and macrocosm — which means any human being, in nature and in the entire universe, and in the three states of aggregation of the physical, the astral, and the mental bodies.

True magic is therefore the high knowledge of the more subtle powers that have not yet been acknowledged by today's science, because scientific methods of scrutiny do not suffice to understand and utilize these powers, even though the laws of magic are analogous to all the official sciences of our world.

Logical reflections and conclusions on the science of magic and its effectiveness not only make the true Hermetic recognize the subtle material powers; they also put him in a position to bring the laws of these powers into harmony with all the official sciences of our planet. With the help of the various keys, the spiritual scientist is even capable of bringing his knowledge to bear in all branches of science and to enlarge and extend them. The knowledge of true magic offers the inventive mind a great many possibilities for technical and material development. Of course, the maturity of a human being is of great importance in this case insofar as he is able to transfer the universal laws of the powers to the material world.

In the following pages of this book, I will deal with different analogies and effects of subtle material powers that assert themselves through manifestations in the three different realms. In other words, I will describe the practical application of magical laws and it will be up to each reader to utilize this knowledge and wisdom for his own purposes.

This clearly shows that magic is a pure metaphysics which may be analyzed in exactly the same way as any field of science dealing with matter, and which can be brought into harmony with natural science. This is to say that metaphysics is an extension of normal physical knowledge of the natural sciences.

There is no magic without mysticism, i.e. no substance without influences, effects and manifestations, since these two fundamental basic concepts are dependent on each other. Magic may not be separated from mysticism, and both have to be dealt with at the same time and in a like manner. In his studies, the Hermetic must always proceed in a magical and mystical manner; that is, he must always bear in mind both quantity and quality, and he must be able to differentiate distinctly between quantity (for example, power in matter and substances) and quality (for example, attributes, effects, influences, and the like). He must never confuse the two concepts if he does not wish to create chaos.

Remember! Magic is quantity and mysticism is quality! When, in the chapters that follow, I speak of quantities, I will always mean magic. When talking about influences, attributes, abilities, virtues, and so forth, I will be referring to mysticism. This has been a universal law from the beginning of the world and it will remain a universal law until its end!

Chapter III
Mysteries of Hermetic Anatomy

In this chapter I will direct the reader's attention from the general challenge of magic and mysticism to the occult anatomy of man, and I will lead him to reflect upon the subject exhaustively from the magico-mystical point of view, which, as regards one's initiation, is the most important viewpoint. One could write many comprehensive volumes on magic and mysticism relating to nature in the mineral, vegetable, and animal kingdoms.

The fourth Tarot card symbolizes the wisdom of man, and therefore it is important that one should learn to know thoroughly, from the magico-mystical point of view, the nature of man, one's own nature, everything one does, and all the functions of one's activities. "Know thyself!" is an important Hermetic axiom which stimulates us to penetrate magically and mystically into the deeper aspects of humankind. Each detail of one's character will then unfold automatically from the knowledge of the functions and principles which I will now describe.

The Mental or Spiritual Body

In my first book, *Initiation Into Hermetics,* I could give only a rough outline of the mental body, the first Tarot card not permitting more than that. In this book I am going to expand the student's knowledge, from both the magical and mystical standpoint, in so far as the functions of the mental or spiritual body are concerned.

The mental body consists of the most subtle substance, also called mental matter. This mental matter is connected to the earth element, to the base material body, due to the cohesive force of that element. The mental body is immortal and subject to neither time nor space. Its basic characteristics allow it to conform to any shape, to adopt any shape. The mental matter, sometimes also called the original or prime matter, consists of two basic forces, the electric and magnetic fluids, both of which are adapted to the mental body's degree of density. The reciprocal activity of the electric and the magnetic fluids in the mental body is called the immortal life.

It is in the mental body that one will find the so-called "I" consciousness, that consciousness of the self which is a union of:

* will power,
* intellect (intelligence), and
* feeling (perception).

If any of these three basic principles is missing, there will be no "I" consciousness, for it is this trinity in the mental body that constitutes the "I" consciousness in the spirit of man. If one or the other of these three principles is disengaged, human consciousness cannot function. The development of these three basic principles depends upon one's general development and maturity.

From the Hermetic point of view, quantity and quality must also be considered in this case:

* The quantity of the will rests upon its power, and its quality rests upon its content.

* The same rule applies to the intellect, which also has its quantitative power and its qualitative form; the quantitative form of the intellect depends upon the perseverance with which all one's intellectual abilities are used, while the

qualitative form determines the spirit's development and degree of maturity through the content of the thoughts.

* The third principle is the emotional life, and it is subject to the same laws; for example, the quantitative side is expressed by the depth and intensity of sensitivity and the qualitative side by the content of the feelings. The power of feeling (or perception) depends upon the level of development of the human being concerned and is of decisive importance.

The Electric and Magnetic Fluids In the Mental Body

These must accomplish other functions besides those mentioned above. And just as everything living can only be maintained by taking in the appropriate nourishment, so the needs of the mental body must also be met. The Hermetic may possibly be engaged with the following question: With what or in what way is the mental body nourished?

As I have previously pointed out,[6] the electro-magnetic fluids in the mental body are constantly in motion because of reciprocity. This condition leads to a certain consumption of both fluids. This consumption is compensated through the impression of the senses from either the mental, astral, or material planes. However, if the senses are over-exerted, a decrease of mental power will result, regardless of which part of the body may be affected.

It should be remembered that in the normal use of the senses, the consequence will be a certain loss of the electro-magnetic fluids, but that this is balanced out by their inductive form; in other words, the mental body receives new spiritual substances via the senses, from which it obtains its

---

[6] In Part I of the author's *Initiation Into Hermetics.*

163

nourishment. Of course, this is not material nourishment; rather, the electro-magnetic fluids of the mental body are constantly recharged by the five senses. Also, the qualitative and quantitative aspects are of great importance in this process, for the mental body gets its quantitative charge through the impression of the senses — that is, it receives its fuel, which again may take certain forms of quality. The qualities that the mental body receives through the impression of the senses depend in principle on the individual's train of thought and, apart from that, on the particular situation which the mental body must endure.

It is recommended that one enrich one's knowledge on this subject by in-depth meditation, because by so doing the Hermetic will discover many mysteries of the spirit which I cannot possibly reveal here. The Hermetic must have a thorough knowledge of the constitution of the mental body and all its functions in order to be able to analyze the microcosm or, to use a modern term, to analyze it by psychoanalysis. His thorough knowledge of the mental body will enable him to utilize either one or the other of its functions and to restore its equilibrium at any time by the appropriate training.

Still with an eye on the electric and magnetic fluids, I should now like to disclose further facts to the Hermetic. Physics has made it known that not only are electricity and magnetism bipolar, but they may be used either constructively or destructively. The same is the case with the electro-magnetic fluids. This bipolarity not only occurs in nature, but, subject to the same laws, in the astral and mental bodies as well. In their constructive activities both fluids are the fortifying principles of the spirit, which means that they represent everything good and noble. The destructive activities of the electro-magnetic fluids bring about the contrary qualities. Both these effects must be completely understood by the Hermetic, and he must work upon both principles, the constructive and destructive alike, by meditation, for they represent what all religious systems as well as the mystics call the good and the evil in man.

The constructive and destructive activities in the mental body have further extensive spheres of activity which I will deal with later. The Hermetic should now devote his attention to the spirit, the "I" consciousness that is the personality. I have noted repeatedly that there is no attribute without power and, vice versa, no power without an attribute. The Hermetic already knows that will, intellect, and feeling constitute the consciousness of man if they work together. If he reflects upon consciousness, the Hermetic will discover that what is generally called consciousness is actually the personality of man in the truest sense of the word.

***

This is the end of the fragment. The recorded tapes were requisitioned when Franz Bardon was arrested in 1958; it was assumed that they were destroyed by the police.

The destruction of the tapes was confirmed a few years ago to Dr. Lumir Bardon, son of Franz Bardon, upon his inquiry.

Dieter Rüggeberg
Wuppertal, December, 1994

The Works of Franz Bardon

Available Through:
Merkur Publishing, Inc.
PO Box 171306
Salt Lake City, UT
USA 84117

In Europe Available Through:
Rüggeberg Verlag
Postfach 13 08 44
D-42035 Wuppertal
Germany

The series of books on Hermetics (Alchemy) by Franz Bardon reveals the Holy Mysteries. They are unique in that they contain theory and practice. It is also important that these works be read and practiced in the proper sequence. Should the reader not do so, he will have great difficulties in understanding the content, even from a philosophical view point; as for the practitioner, he will not progress at all. Therefore, it is advisable for everyone to follow this sequence:

Frabato the Magician
(Introduction)

Though cast in the form of a novel, Frabato the Magician is in fact the spiritual autobiography of Franz Bardon, one of the greatest adepts in the universe.

Set in Dresden, Germany, in the early 1930s, the story chronicles Bardon's magical battles with the members of a powerful black lodge, his escape from Germany during the final days of the Weimar Republic, and the beginning of the spiritual mission which was to culminate in Bardon's classic books on Hermetic magic.

Also included are fragments of The Golden Book of Wisdom, the fourth Tarot card.

Photos, $19.95, 173 pages, softbound, ISBN 1885928157.

Initiation into Hermetics
(Volume I)

A course of magical instruction in ten steps. Theory and practice. Complete revelation of the first Tarot card. From the index:

Part I: Theory
Picture of the magician.
The astral plane.
The elements: Fire, Air, Water and Earth.
The spirit.
Light.
The mental plane.
The Akasha or Etheric principle.
Truth.
Karma, the law of cause and effect.
Religion and God.
The soul or astral body.

Part II: Practice
(1) Though control. Subordination of unwanted thoughts. Self-knowledge or introspection. Conscious breathing and reception of food.
(2) Autosuggestion. Concentration exercises with the five senses. Meditations. Attaining astral and magical balance with respect to the elements. Transmutation of character and temperament.
(3) Concentration exercises with two or three senses at once. Inhaling the elements through the entire body. Impregnation of space.
(4) Transference of consciousness. Accumulation of elements. Production of elemental harmony. Rituals and their practical application.
(5) Space magic. Outward projection of the elements. Preparation for passive communication with the invisible ones.
(6) Preparation to master the Akasha principle. Deliberate induction of trance by means of the Akasha. Deliberate creation of different beings (elementals, larvae, phantoms).

(7) Development of the astral senses by means of the elements: clairvoyance, clairaudience, clairsentience. Creation of elementaries. Magical animation of pictures.

(8) The practice of mental wandering. Mastering the electric and magnetic fluids. Magical influence by means of the elements Preparation of a magic mirror.

(9) The practical use of the magic mirror: clairvoyance, distant effects, different tasks of projection, etc. Deliberate separation of the astral body from the physical one. Magical charging of talismans, amulets and gems.

(10) Elevation of the spirit to higher spheres or worlds. Conscious communication with God. Communication with spirit beings.

Picture of the first Tarot card. One photo of the author. $24.95, 356 pages, softbound, ISBN 1885928122.

The Practice of Magical Evocation
(Volume II)

Complete revelation of the second Tarot card. Instructions for evoking spirit beings from the spheres surrounding us. The author speaks from his own experience!

Part I: Magic
Magical aids: the magic circle, triangle, censer, mirror, lamp, wand, sword, crown, garment, and belt. The pentacle, lamen or seal. The book of magic spells. In the domain of the spirit beings. Advantages and disadvantages of evocational magic. The *"spiritus familiaris"* or serving spirit. Magical evocation. The practice of magical evocation (description of a complete conjuration).

Part II: Hierarchy
(1) The spirits of the four elements.
(2) Intelligences of the zone girdling the earth.
(3) The 360 heads of the zone girdling the earth.
(4) Intelligences of the Moon sphere.
(5) The 72 intelligences of the Mercury sphere.
(6) Intelligences of the Venus sphere.
(7) Genii of the Sun sphere.
(8) Intelligences of the Mars sphere.
(9) Genii of the Jupiter sphere.
(10) The Saturn sphere.
(11) The spheres of Uranus and Pluto.
(12) Communication with spirit beings, genii and intelligences of all spheres through mental travel.
(13) Talismanic magic.

Part III: Illustrations — Seals of Spirit Beings

Picture of the second Tarot card. $44.95, 522 pages, including 148 pages with seals of spirit beings, hardbound, ISBN 1885928130.

The Key to the True Kabbalah
(Volume III)

Complete revelation of the third Tarot card. The cosmic language in theory and practice. The Kabbalist as a sovereign in the micro- and macrocosm.

Part I: Theory — The Kabbalah
Man as a Kabbalist. The laws of analogy. Esotericism of letters. The cosmic language. The magical or Kabbalistic word. The Tetragrammaton. The mantras and tantras. Magical formulas. Theory of Kabbalistic mysticism. Kabbalistic magic.

Part II: Practice
Mysticism of letters. Kabbalistic incantation. Aqua vitae kabbalisticae. Kabbalisticae elementorum. The ten Kabbalistic keys. The Tetragrammaton: Yod-Heh-Vau-Heh. The Kabbalistic fourfold key. The Kabbalistic mysticism of the alphabet. The first key — the simple letters.

Part III: The Magic of Formulas
The Kabbalistic alphabet. The twofold key. The use of the threefold key. The use of the fourfold key. Formulas of the elements. Kabbalistic use of divine names and beings. The Kabbalist as absolute master of the micro- and macrocosm. Through the ages, he who was called "The Master of the Word" was always the highest initiate, the highest priest and the true representative of God.

Picture of the third Tarot card. One photo of the author. $29.95, 286 pages, softbound, ISBN 1885928149.

Franz Bardon: Questions & Answers
By Dieter Rüggeberg

This most recent volume is the first complete new work to appear since Bardon's famous series of books on Hermetics. Compiled by Dieter Rüggeberg from the notes of Bardon's students in Prague, it represents his oral teachings on the nature of the magical universe. Set in the form of questions and answers, this book is an invaluable addition to the Bardon material.

$14.95, 99 pages, softbound, ISBN 1885928114.